D1253887

The Western Frontier Library

(Complete list on pages 171–73)

THE INDIANS AND THE NURSE

The Indians and the Nurse

by Elinor D. Gregg

UNIVERSITY OF OKLAHOMA PRESS : NORMAN

B
G819

To All the Nurses of the Indian Service

Foreword

WHEN I TOLD MY MOTHER that I had decided to take a Red Cross job among the Sioux Indians in South Dakota, she sighed and asked why I wanted to bury myself in the wilds. She had done some pioneering in Colorado Springs in 1882, and having got back to Massachusetts after thirty-five years out West, she couldn't understand my wanting to live outside New England. With all her appreciation of the Boston Symphony and the Boston Art Museum she just couldn't imagine why I chose the wide open spaces. That I found New Englanders stodgy and conventional seemed to her maverick, to put it mildly. She was not given to praise and often made her points with us children by quite salty sayings. On this occasion she said to me, "Well, you have one quality that may stand you in good stead." I, thinking that she was going to mention a good quality (I should have known better), said, "What's that, Mother?" She replied quietly, "You have the courage of ignorance. It may be an asset."

To write this essay in recollection has not been easy because I did not keep a diary. Dates and sequence are not altogether accurate, but this does not purport to be a history. It is my recollection—my impressions at the time were vivid and have stayed with me all these years. I enjoyed my association with the Indian Service. When

I now hear how much is being done for the Indians I realize how limited my work was bound to be. But I knew these limitations forty years ago.

ELINOR D. GREGG

August 25, 1965
Santa Fe, New Mexico

Acknowledgments

I WOULD LIKE TO THANK those who first persuaded me to set down on paper my experiences, primarily Mr. Nicholas Roosevelt and Mr. William Chenery, who convinced me that there was value in my story. Even more than that is the help that Mrs. Anabel Haas gave me. She contributed many hours to going over the process of my proper preparation of the manuscript, helping with the composition, order, and accuracy, and criticizing where necessary. Her interest and enthusiasm were invaluable.

ELINOR D. GREGG

Contents

THE INDIANS AND THE NURSE

I

My Choice in the Nursing Field

AFTER THE FIRST WORLD WAR, I came home from Base Hospital 5 in France, realizing that I must decide what kind of nursing I wanted to spend the rest of my life doing. I had tried industrial nursing in a cotton mill, training school supervising, and hospital management, and none of them really excited my enthusiasm. I did not have to decide immediately; my father was in failing health and I was needed at home with him and my mother. But like the returning soldiers, I had an itching foot. The Red Cross, spending some of their war funds, was engaged in a project to teach and establish public-health nursing, especially in the rural areas. They hired about twenty nurses who had been overseas and sent them with Chautauqua entertainers to tell the Chautauqua audiences about their overseas experiences and about the value of having a county public-health nurse.

I had done visiting nursing in my training in Waltham, Massachusetts, and in 1920 public-health nursing did not have a well-defined program, though it included visiting patients in their homes. There were programs, but the policies were just being formulated.

The medical profession as a group was not interested in preventive medicine. The present interest in this field has come about in the last forty years.

But to go back to Chautauqua—I signed on. I never had done any public speaking but was not daunted by that. I was to make the same speech ninety-two times in ninety-three days, and I thought it would come easier as I went along. I had heard that practice makes perfect. Anyway, June, 1919, found me in Washington at the Red Cross and then out to Lincoln, Nebraska, to join a "five-day circuit team." My co-entertainers were a troupe of five young girls who played the violin or cello and a young man who accompanied on the piano and was "the boss." They were all of college age, and I suppose that I was a balance wheel if not exactly a chaperone. We toured through Kansas, Colorado, and one town, Farmington, in New Mexico.

We had our tent crew, and occasionally we met the other four teams of entertainers on our circuit. Because we were the fifth-day performers, we always helped take down the big tent after the evening performance. My speech came in the afternoon. I wore a white silk uniform (no "drip-dry" in those days), a Red Cross nurse's cap, and the regulation white oxfords and white silk stockings. I suppose my speech is all tucked away in my skull somewhere, but I doubt if it could ever be hauled out again. What I remember are the funny things that happened.

In Genoa, Nebraska, a bush pilot was giving airplane rides for one dollar, and when the plane revved up its engine, the entire audience in the tent left me alone on the platform and trooped out to see the plane. So I waited until they drifted back in and began again where I had left off.

In Grafton, Kansas, seven white hens came walking into the tent, down the middle aisle, up to the front, and flew onto the back of the empty seats, tucked their heads under their wings, and slept through my "war experience" very comfortably.

4

In Durango, Colorado, it was hot—very hot—and I made the mistake of putting a little too much blood and mud and bombs into my speech, and two women fainted. I had to go on with the speech instead of following my nursing instincts to stop talking and take care of the fainters.

We traveled by cars and buses, occasionally making long hops by train. We stayed in small hotels and private homes; there were no motels in those days. When I got back to Brookline, Massachusetts, I was well cured of my itching foot.

I don't believe I sold much county public-health nursing except to myself, but I saw a lot of western rural U.S.A. and knew that I preferred it to New England. However, I stayed at home and took a four-month course at Simmons College in public-health nursing. The Red Cross paid for it, and I promised to take a Red Cross job when I could leave my parents.

The following summer I took a short-term Red Cross job teaching home nursing in a rural county in New Hampshire. My sister had a summer farm farther north in New Hampshire, and my parents were staying there for the summer. By that time I had a Model T Ford runabout, so I ran about five villages teaching how to give bed baths and enemas; bandaging, sterilizing gauze in the oven, taking temperatures and pulses and respirations, and bathing babies. On Saturday evenings I went up to South Tamworth for weekends with my family.

The following winter I stayed at home. My father died in the spring, and my mother went to live with a nurse who took several elderly ladies to room and board. And then I was looking about for a permanent job under the Red Cross.

Miss Elizabeth Fox was director of public-health nursing at the American Red Cross in Washington in October,

5

1922. I visited her, and she asked me if I would go to South Dakota on the Rosebud and Pine Ridge reservations.

From Miss Fox I learned that Mr. Charles E. Burke was commissioner of Indian affairs; he had seen a Red Cross nurse functioning in Pierre, South Dakota, after the war and decided that the Indian Service would profit by that type of employee. There was no superimposed program, it was nebulous.

Miss Fox told me, further, that the Interior Department was under Dr. Hubert Work, who was interested in improving the health service among the Indians. Congress at that time was not interested in supplying funds, so Dr. Work decided that if he could not get more salary for the doctors, he would begin with nurses. He could not get the then Indian Committee of Congress interested in that, either, so he went to the Red Cross to see if they would loan the Indian Bureau three nurses—one to make a general survey of health service, and two less experienced nurses, one to be stationed on a small reservation and one on a large reservation.

Miss Florence Patterson, a public-health nurse of wide experience, was to make the general survey of the various Indian Service territories. I did not have an opportunity to talk with her. Her report, which I saw two years later, portrayed existing conditions, and I suppose she gave some indication of what could be established instead of telling what she found. Her report was so hot that it was buried in the files.

Miss Augustine Stoll had been chosen for the five hundred Jicarilla Apaches in Dulce, New Mexico, and I accepted the larger territory of the two Sioux reservations, the Pine Ridge and the Rosebud, which were contiguous. There were seven thousand Sioux on the Pine Ridge and six thousand on the Rosebud Reservation. The territory extended approximately ninety miles north and south and

6

two hundred miles east and west along the South Dakota and Nebraska boundary lines from Chadron, Nebraska, to the Missouri River near Gregory, South Dakota. There was to be no transportation furnished except that I could catch a ride with other reservation personnel. I had my open Ford runabout and decided to drive from Boston to Rosebud Agency in November. The agencies would supply the gasoline and oil and other services for the car. The Red Cross would supervise from the Minneapolis headquarters.

Miss Fox's last words to me were, "See what you can do to give the Indians better health care and education." For a public-health nurse, it was a wide-open task.

I had never been in South Dakota; however, it was just north of Nebraska, and I had seen quite a little of rural Nebraska and Kansas during my Chautauqua experience with the Red Cross. I knew South Dakota was similar, perhaps colder and less prosperous among the white settlers, but the government employees must have some place to live and work. Therefore, my drive across half the country was just one day at a time, and I enjoyed each day.

I started from Boston, followed the road maps to Pittsburgh, into Ohio and Indiana, thence to Chicago, where my brother was working. Ohio and Indiana were new to me. The farms were smaller than western ranches; they looked quite prosperous compared with the ranches of eastern Colorado and western Kansas.

My brother did not then drive a car but had kindly offered to go with me from Chicago to Sioux Falls, South Dakota, and take the train back. All this was agreed upon by letter before I left Boston.

Although it was raining part of the way, the trip was a pleasure, becoming more enjoyable as the open spaces increased. The brick farmhouses of Ohio were quite close to the brick roads, which were narrow but better than the

7

mud of rural Pennsylvania. I had road maps from the gas stations and worked out my route in detail one day at a time. I was rather worried about getting through Chicago but wired my brother from Gary, Indiana, to meet me at the La Salle Street station at noon the next day. I expected to arrive in Chicago about 11 A.M. as I could start early. I probably could have found a better approach to Chicago, but it looked to be the shortest route. I remember the miles of city streets and the early morning trucks of south Chicago. Finally I found a parking lot near the La Salle Street station about 11 A.M. I dawdled around, window shopping for an hour, and then headed back toward the station. There on the street corner opposite the station I met my brother, suitcase in hand. We walked to the parking lot and set off for Minneapolis, where I was to report to the Red Cross office in whose territory I would be working.

Miss Ahrens was in charge of the Minneapolis office, but the field supervisor, Miss McArdle, was not there when I arrived. This visit took half a day. Miss Ahrens knew even less about the job than I had learned in Washington, so my brother and I headed for Sioux Falls, South Dakota. The route I don't remember, but we had a delightful spell of Indian summer for late October.

When we reached Sioux Falls, my brother left me, and I went on, crossing the Missouri River at Chamberlain over to Presho, where I turned south to Winner, South Dakota. This town was on a direct road to Rosebud. When I got to Winner, I found myself one day behind time, so I wired the Rosebud superintendent that I would be there the next day. It was a sixty-mile trip, but by starting before dawn I arrived by noon, glad to get there.

The whole trip had taken eleven days at twenty to thirty miles an hour. Nowadays one could do it in about five days.

8

II

Rosebud—First Impression

ROSEBUD RESERVATION in South Dakota in November did not live up to its name. Gone were the lovely wild pink roses that colored the plain in June. Pine Ridge lived up to its name both winter and summer. The rocky hills were covered with jack pines—very Japanese looking in effect. This countryside was infinitely more to my liking than the purlieus of South Boston where I had done visiting nursing. It was better than other places I knew—Cleveland, Ohio, or the country area of New Hampshire, or the France of army days, but how had I come to my decision to take a Red Cross job among the Sioux Indians?

I arrived at the agency, and looking at it as my home and working center, I was more concerned with the spirit of the group than with the physical details. The agency headquarters looked barren, but the sidewalks and a central green plaza represented some effort toward pleasantness, and there were red brick buildings for office and living quarters. The agency was surrounded by low hills stretching out to barren plains; there were two dry creekbeds, one to the south and one to the east. I did not even consider whether or not I liked it. There I was; whether I liked it or not made no difference.

My first introduction at the agency was, of course, to

the Superintendent, who turned me over to the doctor. The doctor was lame—my guess was a repaired clubfoot. He said he did not know what I was supposed to do but thought that I had better carry a large stock of aspirin, sulphur ointment for the itch, Argyol for inflamed eyes, oil of wintergreen for rheumatism, wild cherry cough syrup, Epsom salts, corrosive sublimate (a disinfectant), and green soap. I devised some standing orders which he signed.

After talking with the doctor, seeing his wife—the hospital nurse—and being introduced to most of the "employees," I went back to the Superintendent and suggested that I begin by getting acquainted with the Indian children, doing a health examination on all the school children—vision tests, hearing tests, and weight and physical anomalies. The doctor was responsible for giving smallpox vaccinations and diphtheria toxin-antitoxin. There was nothing to do to prevent or control measles, whooping cough, or scarlet fever. There were four hundred children whose parents were willing to have them at a boarding school where they would be fed and clothed entirely at government expense, so I proposed to live at the boarding school in order to get to know the children—their physical condition as well as their psychology.

Like most federal organizations, the Indian Service is a closed group, dealing as best it can with variegated problems, with inadequate funds. To me it was an education. The education had begun with my drive from Boston to South Dakota, about nineteen hundred miles in a Model T open-air Ford in late October at about twenty miles an hour.

Two days after I arrived, we had a good dose of "squaw winter"—the first fall of snow. I was installed in a room in the employees' building with a soft-coal stove for heat. Knowing that I came from Boston—the center of the "effete East" to the "rugged West" of South Dakota, all the employees expected me to shrivel up and leave forthwith. The waited in vain, not knowing that I had spent the first twenty years of my life in Colorado with soft-coal stoves and kerosene lamps. There was electricity at the agency headquarters, but it had a tendency to fail and leave us with candles or a kerosene lamp. I bought both at the general store. I had packed some blankets in my trunk, which arrived by express some three weeks later. Meanwhile, I was supplied with old army blankets and promptly settled in.

There was a hotel at the agency, operated mostly for transients and singletons, where I got my meals. We had good milk, homemade bread, hot cereal, beef stew, pot roast, and occasional pork chops. For dessert we had pie (apple, squash, and raisin). No lettuce or fresh vegetables or fruit, but fairly good canned stuff and winter root vegetables and winter squash. The general store carried apples, bananas, and oranges most of the time, so despite our being forty miles from a head of lettuce, we made out fairly well, though I did long for salad occasionally.

I had no way of cooking so much as a cup of coffee. It was before the days of "coffee breaks." We worked from eight o'clock to five o'clock, with an hour off for dinner from twelve o'clock to one. The mail truck came in from Crookston, Nebraska, twenty-five miles south, about half-past twelve noon, and I went to the general store to get my mail just before one o'clock.

The Superintendent of the Rosebud Agency was the boss; he had to supervise a wide variety of services: education, a boarding school for three hundred children from the fourth grade through high school; day schools, first three grades, about four of them at the different centers of Indian population; an agricultural agent, who was supposed to

11

teach the Indians to farm, to irrigate where water was available, to look after the cattle, and to mend the barbed-wire fences, and give out the government rations to the old and needy; an engineer to keep the water pumps and electric systems going; and a garage mechanic to keep the cars going.

The Superintendent also administered the hospital, the medical field service, the accounts of government funds, the census roll of Indians, the judiciary, law and order, and the care of indigents, jokingly called "the old and indignant Indians." It was a totalitarian state, and the Superintendent was often referred to as the "Czar." His helpers were farmers, teachers, doctors, lawyers, police, nurses, mechanics, and accountants—a little world carrying out the laws made in Washington by Congress. A microcosm of government for, but not by, the people. The Superintendent was supposedly dedicated to the education of the Indians in the American Way of Life as laid down by Congress. It was teaching both by precept and example. No alcoholic beverages, smoking (for women), or swearing were countenanced officially, and the Indians were pretty sharp to report on the employees of Uncle Sam. They watched for any aberrations of conduct. A "good employee" was a pretty strait-laced person, and the missionaries of various denominations kept a running watch on everybody, including each other. Yet such was the denominational fervor in those days that the employees could not go to church and still have any influence with all Indians. If you went to a Presbyterian service, you were not acceptable in the tipi of an Episcopalian Indian, nor would the Catholic Indians accept the teaching of an employee who worshiped with the Protestants. Therefore, the "good employee" was a strait-laced, sometimes narrow-minded, quite morally conventional person who could live without church worship.

12

Remember, this was forty years ago. In the fall of 1960 I went to an Indian Service banquet, and Indians and whites had drinks in the bar together before dinner. Times do change!

But to return to the Rosebud Reservation of forty years ago: To the employees I was just a new experiment. They were the regulars; I was an "outlander," a Red Cross nurse from Massachusetts. No one knew what I was supposed to do. They were politely interested, not at all hostile. Since I didn't know myself just what I was going to do, the time I had off from duty hours I spent getting acquainted.

I had the feeling that nobody thought I would stick with it. The employees knew all the pitfalls—the cold, the blizzards, the wind and dust and heat, the roads with ruts over fifteen inches deep with centers so high you had to crawl under the car and dig them out with a screw driver instead of a shovel; the mud holes and slippery gumbo, the sand pits, the so-called "main-traveled trail," which phrase was so vague you had to hope your interpretation was inspired concerning which track had been traveled most recently or most often.

The Indians traveled mostly in Studebaker farm wagons with a pair of horses. The wife sat beside her husband, the grandmothers and children in the wagonbed. I was laughed at because I sat beside the doctor when we made a call together. I learned later that it had a sexual connotation to the Indians. But they knew I was unaware of this, hence the laughter. There were few automobiles, though quite a few Indians knew how to drive well enough. There were government cars for the police, the farmers, the school supervisor, and of course the Superintendent and the doctor. If I had not had my own little model T, I would have had to catch a ride with some other person and could not have visited the Indians in their homes.

13

III

I Get Started

AT THAT TIME, public-health nursing as part of the state public-health programs included school nursing follow-up and school health examinations. A nurse's school health examination included weighing and measuring, giving vision and hearing tests, and checking for gross muscular disabilities, enlarged neck glands, enlarged tonsils, mouth breathing, and chronic or frequent colds. The immunization program was against diphtheria and smallpox. There was antitetanus serum, but it was expensive and given only when cases developed.

The State Anti-Tuberculosis Society was trying to encourage the finding and hospitalization of active cases. Checking up the contacts was just a beginning. Health education was only starting and had to do with personal cleanliness largely. A program of examining well babies was just being inaugurated and had not jelled into the present-day program of monthly visits to a well-baby clinic. Clinics for sick babies were few and far between.

When I began thinking of what I could do to fit this picture of public-health nursing into the medical service as I found it functioning on the Rosebud, I decided to try out various activities as the opportunities arose. There were no clinics; the practice of medicine was either in the hospital or in the home. My public-health function did not appeal to the doctor as feasible.

Most of the hospital cases were obstetrics, fractures, and other accidents, and the aged who had no family to care for them. The home care was by call from the Indians and might be anything from accidents to hemorrhages of the lung. Diarrhea and gastritis were frequent. The policy of the Indian Bureau was to leave the adult active tuberculosis cases in the home and put only school children in specially designated sanatorium schools.

I found myself the only graduate nurse for six thousand Indians. The doctor's wife, an undergraduate nurse, was the practical nurse who worked only in the hospital. She had two Indian women as attendants under her tutelage, plus an Indian cook and an Indian janitor. The practical nurse got about $600 a year, the attendants about $240, and the cook probably $480 with food and lodging.

Mr. McGregor, the superintendent, wanted me to spend a week with him looking in on his office work of interviewing the Indians who came to see him on all sorts of matters. This served a dual purpose: He would get acquainted with me, and I would get some idea of what went on in the agency office. So that was my first week of activity. At the end of that week, we decided that in order to begin to get acquainted with the Indians, I had better go to the government boarding school and make health examinations of the children. I would retain my room at the agency but temporarily live at the boarding school.

I took a few clothes and my pocketbook over to mission, where the boarding school was located, and was introduced to the school employees. I lived at the Employees' Club and began doing the conventional school examinations. Although my main purpose was to get acquainted with the children, incidentally I discovered the general attitudes of the teachers and matrons toward the children. I also learned about the organization of the school activities.

The children were housed in three dormitories. Big girls, small girls, and boys.

There were no active tuberculosis cases in the boarding school, but there were so many children with inflamed eyes being treated for trachoma that I was shocked. Perhaps most of the conjunctivitis was due to the wind full of sand and a secondary infection of the corneal ulcer, but there were no sulpha drugs and no cortizone for the eye conditions.

I stayed at the mission for six weeks. The children were under the care of dormitory matrons. The girls' matron was one of the most competent women I met in the service, Miss Della Fisher. She knew her girls and understood them; she knew their adolescent psychology, was kind and firm, and made her commands stick. She never wielded authority just for the sake of authority. She didn't quite understand the purpose of my being there, but we got along very happily. She had a good sense of humor, had been in the service many years, and took all the vagaries of the service without comment or scorn. It was a demanding job, and she met it well.

The boys' matron was Mrs. Bruce, another competent woman and one who liked boys. She was the product of a Chippewa Indian and Scot marriage. Her husband was the boys' advisor, who handled the discipline of a large group of half-grown boys. He was quiet; the boys liked him. He was something of a jack-of-all-trades in the engine room, the barn, and as a carpenter.

There was a large dining room and kitchen in a separate building for the children. The school building was also separate from the dormitories. For the children older than

16

ten, the day was divided into a half day in school and a half day on work detail.

As I recall, the boys worked only out of doors on the farm, the girls indoors in the dining room, kitchen, laundry, and at the girls' dormitories. If the girls worked for the teachers, they were paid a small amount, about twenty cents an hour. This pattern was based upon the plan of Hampton Institute for Negroes in Virginia.

The first thing that surprised me was my inability to connect Indian names with faces. The names were all translations of their Sioux Indian names—James Runs-along-the-Edge, Paul Never-Misses-a-Shot, Maria Keen-Knife, Sarah Jumps-Over. It took me a long time to learn them. There were quite a number of French names, the Roubidoux, the La Pointes, some English, Scotch, and German names, which of course were easy.

After six weeks at the government boarding school, I went down to the Catholic boarding school, where there were three hundred children. I stayed there eight weeks doing another round of health examinations. By that time spring was beginning, and I started to visit in the homes of three districts, Blackpipe, Parmelee, and Wood. These districts, twenty to thirty miles from headquarters, were one long day's journey for the Indian horses, one-half day by Ford car at twenty miles and hour. For any trip to see the superintendent or to visit relatives, the Indians camped out. It was a great pleasure to them but hard on their crops and cattle.

But the Indians loved to travel. They prized their canvas tents. To hitch up their horses to the Studebaker farm wagon, hang a couple of pails under the wagon, load into the wagonbed the children, bedding, food, grandparents, and grain for the horses and start for the agency headquarters twenty miles away was a real pleasure and relief

17

from the monotony of staying at home. Perhaps they only went to see some relatives a few miles from home, but to be on the move was a natural longing to the Sioux. If they had planted any corn, beans, or squash, they hoped the stray cattle would not break down the barbed-wire enclosure; they also hoped for rain in their absence but did not feel obliged to stay home on that account.

Wealth was expressed in horseflesh in 1922. The Sioux were good horsemen but callous in their treatment and training of the wild broncos. They had no grain for the animals and depended on wild pasture and alfalfa hay.

IV

Field Matrons

AFTER FINISHING WITH THE INSPECTIONS of school children I wanted to get acquainted with adults. To visit the field matron would offer this opportunity.

The field matron's function in the districts was as advisor to the married women, and since this was the only work comparable to public-health nursing, I felt I should know their plan of work. By visiting with them, I could see the home conditions of the Indians. This service was very badly organized. It was under the superintendent, not confined to medical work, and each field matron put the emphasis on her own interest. I had already learned that the government was planning to abolish the field-matron service and use the money for public-health nurses. That this was to be done did not make me intensely popular with the field matrons. The general philosophy behind their service was that any good woman could teach every good woman what all good women should know. They were supposed to encourage cleanliness in the log houses, cleanliness of the person, care of babies and children, making of clothing and bedding, canning and preserving food, crocheting, nursing, and cooking. I quote from the Washington letter of instructions to field matrons:

The position of field matron is much more than a

job. It is an opportunity for service to others; an opportunity for self-sacrifice in the interest of humanity; and for the exercise of the highest attributes of mind and soul in a pre-eminent cause. The position should be filled only by women who have the desire and the aptitude to teach the things that influence lives for good and fill them with higher aspirations.

No woman should seek or hold the position of field matron who is not endowed with physical strength, with strong moral and mental force, and with the real missionary spirit—a real spirit of helpfulness that finds expression in a fervent desire to better the conditions of a worthy race that is struggling upward to a realm of higher life, for without these qualifications, the duties will be uncongenial and success cannot be attained. The material remuneration is not large and the discouragements and adversities are many. The rewards are chiefly in the sacrifices.

The letter went on to define the many duties. Tanning hides and making moccasins were indigenous skills, and of course beadwork was also. Long hours went into making the Indian costumes used in ceremonial dances. Making patchwork quilts was easily accomplished. The Indian women did lovely quilting; they scarcely needed teaching.

The first of my three district visits was to Blackpipe. The white settlers called the nearby cluster of stores Norris. There was an Indian day school there, a district farmer, and the field matron. Quite a few Indians lived within one mile or two of the government buildings. The field matron had no transportation but could often catch a ride with the farmer or school teacher when cases of sickness were reported. The official instructions to field matrons on health and sanitation read as follows:

20

Health and Sanitation: To cooperate in all health and sanitary matters with the physician, assisting in his work under his instructions; to report all cases of illness and of conditions detrimental to health and sanitation; to advise expectant mothers, rendering assistance in confinement and in the care of infants and children, and the sick; to instruct the family with respect to the proper disposal of human waste, rubbish and garbage, and with regard to the importance or protection from flies, mosquitoes, vermin, and other sources for the prevention of dangerous communicable diseases.

The saving of Indian babies and how to keep them well should be the chief concern of field matrons, but it is also important that they shall do all in their power to prevent and combat tuberculosis, trachoma, and every other disease, and to relieve the sufferings of the afflicted; to oppose the liquor curse, and the use of every harmful drug or drink; and to exert their influence against every habit that handicaps in the race of life.

If Government aid is necessary to bring health out of disease and squalor, it should not be withheld, but good results if obtained will scarcely continue unless the Indian parents exchange indolence for industry and are awakened to the use and beauty of personal and environing cleanliness.

This campaign for better babies, for the rescue of a race, calls for redoubled energy and zeal throughout the service, for it means physical and personal work and tireless patience. It is a well-nigh stupendous task, but will be a glorious one if we can make successful headway.

21

While all this is good advice to read, without transportation at your command it is impossible to plan for adequate follow-up. It became a hit-or-miss program when the Indians lived more than one mile away from the field matron. This was the situation at Blackpipe. Miss Rasch had no clinic room. Her three-room cottage was her home, and she did not enjoy sharing it with sick Indians. I did not wonder that she resented my intrusion for three weeks as a visitor. My Red Cross status was no pleasure to her, and I am afraid that being able to visit the Indians in my car with me only emphasized her feelings of frustration concerning her ability to conduct her job adequately. She could advise the mother to use sulphur ointment and wash the bedclothes, but there was no way that she could supervise the carrying out of her instructions. Poor woman, I felt sorry for her. She was withdrawn and unco-operative with the school teacher and the farmer. When I used a wash tub in her kitchen to give a sulphur bath to a terribly infected schoolboy, to say that she didn't like it is to put it mildly.

The field matrons at Parmelee and Wood were married to the respective farm agents, which gave them a head start over poor Lottie Rasch at Blackpipe. She had no transportation, and unless the farm agent or the day-school teacher wanted her help, she was sunk. She was a very negative personality. She kept her three-room house very tidy, but her program consisted mostly of collecting information that she could get from one source or another about sexual misconduct. She knew how to can fruits and vegetables, and the Indian women would come to her for jars and lids and new rubbers, but her major activity was bedding. She had quilting frames and encouraged the making of lovely patchwork quilts. She gave out aspirin and castor oil, and sulphur ointment for scabies, but that was about the extent of her health interest. She had a telephone that sometimes worked so that she could call the doctor for accidents and sickness. Tetanus was prevalent around Blackpipe, but the matrons took it all quite lightly, and no shots were given as a routine preventive immunization.

I saw one little four-year-old boy die in convulsion. There was no serum available at the hospital, and to get it from Sioux Falls would have taken at least five days. The child died before it came.

Of course, Lottie saw that I could not do quilting, and I saw that Lottie could not do nursing. While I was at Black-pipe the farm agent over at White River died, and Lottie was very interested in going to the funeral. It was sixty miles away, and also the day was about 60 degrees below zero. But Lottie thought we ought to go, so we went—in my Model T runabout with celluloid side curtains and no heater. The ground was frozen too hard to dig a grave, so there could be no interment. They left the coffin in the woodshed until spring, when a grave could be dug.

That was the day I found out that at 60 degrees below, you were better off if you took off the fan belt. As it was, the radiator, in spite of a couple of gunny sacks tied on it, froze solid, and we boiled all the way going and coming home; I used three kettles of boiling water when I got home before I could drain the radiator. To leave it frozen all night would have meant getting a new engine block for sure. By putting an old army blanket over the radiator and adding boiling water, we finally got it unfrozen.

The second field matron I visited was Mrs. MacDonald, at Wood. Her husband was the farm agent, so she could commandeer some transportation. She was a good house-keeper and cook and was more knowledgeable about sickness than Lottie, having done some practical nursing for a country doctor in Minnesota. She was a pretty good midwife, and as Wood was thirty miles away from the hospital, she found it more practical to help the Indian women have their babies at home. She had done a lot toward breaking down the old-fashioned practice of putting the new mother and baby in a small hut or tent away from the main house, winter or summer. It was she who told me about the old custom of delivery, in which the mother, after the baby came, walked around a pole until there was a circle of blood around it. This was supposed to get rid of all the placenta and purify the blood. But many women were so depleted that they never improved; an old tuberculosis infection could flare up, and often both mother and baby died.

Mrs. MacDonald had an imperfection in her speech, but that did not hinder her talking. She had a pot of coffee, as strong as lye, on the back of the stove all day long. I will never forget that coffee. She was a Swede from Minnesota, married to a Scotchman. I enjoyed my visit with Mrs. MacDonald. She knew her Indians, had taught them to depend on her, and really carried out a program—come hell or high water.

Another thing I remember while at Wood was seeing a horse commit suicide. It had got tangled in a barbed-wire fence. It was lying down, beating its head on the frozen ground. Everyone there said nothing could be done for it. It had lost any ability to respond to the human touch. Next morning it was dead.

My third visit was to the Gardners at Parmelee. This station was only fifteen miles from the agency; therefore, it was much easier to conduct the business needing the approval of the superintendent. And the Indians living so near the agency could get their requests dealt with more promptly. The Gardners were elderly and had a good deal of poise and knowledge of the Indian Service. They were relatively near retirement age (seventy-two years of age

24

or thirty years of service at that time). Mrs. Gardner, in a very lady-like way, was the pants of the family and kept poor old Pa humping on her business as well as his. They were near enough to the hospital to be able to ignore most of the health problems, so Mrs. Gardner concentrated on food problems, canning and drying food. She also made up layettes for the new-born. She was tall and energetic, with hair faultlessly curled, nails manicured, house spotless, and her work routine fitted to the convenience of living without spoiling her style of living. It is true that their door was never closed to Indians, but after five o'clock any service usually could be postponed until the next morning. Their attitude toward me was "poor thing, she will never last; we don't have to worry about her work because the Indian office won't get around to any such change as public-health nurses very soon." And if the top doctor, Robert E. Lee Newburne, in Washington, had not died, they would have been right.

V

My Nursing Care Opportunities

AFTER FINISHING MY VISITS to the field matrons, I felt that I had learned a lot about Indians and the Indian Service. I knew that organized health teaching was a far cry on the horizon. Mr. McGregor wanted me to have some sort of workroom, so he turned one of the small houses in "Indian Row" over to me as quarters and clinic room at the agency.

The cottage was a three-room affair—a living room used as a clinic room, a bedroom, a kitchen, a Chick Sales, a box of soft coal, and a pile of kindling wood on the back stoop. The clinic room had a "base burner" that required anthracite coal, but if carefully managed would hold overnight. If it did not hold over, it was the devil and all to clean it and start a new fire. So that was the first anxiety of the day. The kitchen stove rarely held over, but it burned soft coal and was easy to make up every morning. I had oatmeal, eggs, toast, jam, and coffee for breakfast and went over to the hotel for dinner and supper. I was too tired or lazy to cook for myself regularly, but I could always have enough canned goods to get a meal. A bath was the real problem, a wash tub full of water warmed on the kitchen stove. There were just twenty-four inches of plumbing in the house, a twelve-inch waste pipe from the kitchen sink outdoors and a twelve-inch pipe bringing cold water to the kitchen faucet. There was a dining table with four chairs. I don't seem to

26

remember much about the housekeeping details. I could hire an Indian woman to scrub the floor; there were two pieces of carpet and a bed in the bedroom and some kitchen chairs and a chiffonier. In the clinic room were a table, desk, cot, and rocking chair.

This cottage had been used by an Indian policeman whose ten children had died of tuberculosis. It was all painted fresh for me, with a sign reading "Red Cross Health Station" on the front porch. It is now called the Gregg Health Station.

In those days the Red Cross public-health nurse was practically free lance—trying to create a demand for the benefits she had to offer. She had to sell her services to the patient, to the community, and to the doctors. I knew what activities I was supposed to establish, but just how should I go about it on an Indian reservation? Theoretically, I could visit patients in homes; I could accompany patients to medical care; I could arrange clinics and conferences; I could make speeches to groups; I could inspect schools to check on the health of individual children and the environmental sanitation and follow up on the findings. But which of these activities would produce "a program" of value to, and understood by, the Indians and acceptable to the Indian Service was up to me to decide. The medical world of that day was only beginning to be enlightened concerning preventive medicine. Doctors were rather scornful of the encroachment of nurses and sanitarians into the medical field. I had the support of the reservation superintendent from the beginning—without that I would have foundered more than I did.

In February, 1923, I had the pleasure of a visit from the Red Cross area supervisor, Miss Ellen McArdle. I had four months' experience to talk with her about—the school examination to get acquainted with the Indian children; the few speeches made to Indian women; the lack of group organization among the women; the need for getting sick Indians to surgical care; the home visits on request by the Indians or on reports of the other employees or the superintendent; and the field-matron services.

Miss McArdle did not entirely approve of my giving out medicines on standing orders from the doctors. I felt that she thought I should be organizing my future activities along different lines. She interviewed the superintendent and the doctor and presented to the doctor a plan of having regular children's clinics at the day schools. If there had been ample medical service, it could have been tried, but with only one doctor it seemed quite futile. There were too many emergencies to keep the doctor away. Unless food was going to be served, or unless there was a drastic need for medical care, the Indian women would not make a two-mile trip. It just didn't look feasible to the doctor or to me or to Mr. McGregor. The fact that I would soon be going over to the Pine Ridge Reservation was an added reason for not starting that type of program. We didn't try it. I continued to deal with individual problems as they came to me or were sent to me by Mr. McGregor and the doctor.

I became so troubled about the lack of care for the tuberculosis cases that I decided to see if the South Dakota State Anti-Tuberculosis Society could be persuaded to put on a diagnostic clinic. They agreed to send a chest specialist for a two-day clinic. It seemed rather footless, but it made good publicity for the state association. The Indians, old and young, flocked to be examined. A chest specialist arrived; he listened to about one hundred and twenty chests in a day and was exhausted after two days. The Indians loved it. Mr. McGregor had an issue of beef for a midday meal and appointed certain women to cook. One of the field matrons supervised the food preparation. I got the patients ready for the doctor. We peeled off layers of clothes. Most of the women were sewed into their garments; one woman had on ten cotton dresses. The men had no less than three shirts, often more. It was a smelly job, but it *was* a Public Health Effort! The specialist listened to their chests and recommended certain ones for X ray, but as we had no X ray and they would have to travel either to Pierre or to Winner, money would have to be found. The net result was a lot of opinion about healed lesions, but of course it was really wasted effort as far as individual cases were concerned. I knew it, but it did seem worthwhile to get the State Health people involved somehow.

How I longed for some definite information or technical knowledge that could be applied. The Indians needed food, fuel, and less exertion; they needed cleanliness and some knowledge of germs. All the things that had come slowly to educated white people, the Indians needed ten times as much. Soap and water were hard to come by; vitamins had not yet been discovered. The mothers used condensed milk for the babies' food, but there was no refrigeration other than the windowsill. Sanitation, that is outdoor toilets, were conspicuous by their absence. The prairie offered a good deal of privacy around the house, and dogs and pigs were good scavengers. There was not much typhoid, or at least it escaped diagnosis.

The older Indian women gathered herbs for medicinal use, and there were Indian medicine men who used bears' claws and deer hooves as necklaces (fetishes against disease). Sweat baths were popular with the older men. They made a sort of willow frame over a pile of stones heated by a fire. Then they put the fire out with water, covered the frame with bed quilts, and crawled into the hot steaming tent or wickiup, and when they began to faint with sweating, they came out in the cold air. If they could either get

29

snow or jump into a creek they did that. It was the same general principal as the Swedish or Finnish bathhouses.

They had some sort of herb that they used for pus infections, but I never knew what it was. Also they were quite clever about psychosomatic symptoms. Private ceremonials and dances were held. Most of their dances were displays of muscular skill and endurance. Perhaps some of them had sexual connotations, but I drew no such inference from their imitations of animals. The mission women were dead set against the dances, objecting to them as forms of bestiality. Considering that it was only about one hundred years since the Indians had adopted the Mother Hubbard dress of the missionaries and Levi and shirts of frontiersmen, I found the beaded-buckskin dance costumes of the women and the painted bodies and skin breech clouts of the men perfectly decent. Their passion for eagle feathers held on, and the war bonnet was highly prized. They used turkey feathers to decorate their ten-gallon sombreros. But all this was not called culture by the white people; it was Indian and therefore not desirable to approve.

The last Sioux uprising had taken place in 1898, only a short thirty years before. Led by a Pine Ridge named Crazy-Horse, it had been put down by the army. The result had been some Indians killed but more fear of heavy-handed action on the part of the government. A good many of the older Indians remembered the Indian wars and Custer's last stand. The younger men who had been taken away from their families and had been sent to boarding schools in the East came home because they were more comfortable in Indian culture, but quite understanding that change would wipe that out.

The Congressional policy of substituting education for confinement on reservations had been going on for fifty years, and results were beginning to show unmistakably.

30

There were Sioux Indians from Montana to Minnesota, some forty thousand of them. The Dakotans were the biggest groups, but their own original culture was almost all gone, and they were adrift without much sense of security or individual responsibility. They had heard so much talk of abuse by the government that they were convinced that the government could and should be made to take care of them. The years in government boarding schools where they were fed and clothed did not prepare them to use their land or their education.

There were a few self-reliant men who made a living from cattle and the soil. There were a few who learned and practiced some sort of trade and were good laborers. One-fourth Indian blood entitled them to "Indian Rights." Their names were on the rolls. They were sometimes quite competent, but often they were wily rascals. You had the feeling that they learned trickery from the white people; they did not have to keep promises to white people. Often to avoid a promise they would say "mebbe so," meaning I won't, but it was not polite to say so. Sometimes they would meet you half-way, but usually not.

They all liked a joke. To see you stuck in a mud puddle was more of a joke than an opportunity to earn a little by pulling you out with a lasso. I quickly learned self-reliance.

But they liked a cheerful smile as part of the sauce of life. And I liked their smiles too. They knew it and would ask favors of a ride or cod-liver oil for tanning hides, with ingratiating smiles. It was an exercise of wits, and they often won the contest. To just give them a flat "no" labeled you as impolite or a sorehead or both. I had been brought up to consider an evasive answer a near lie and certainly a sin.

I learned a great deal from my Indian friends. They liked

31

me because I smiled and would listen to them with respect. Like all people subjected to massive direction, they read your intention from subtle signs in face or gestures that you were unconscious of. All these appreciations between us were part of what added spice to my life.

Struggle with the elements of weather, wind, and Ford cars was another source of challenge, but there was also the feeling that I was not getting anywhere, not achieving much of my avowed purpose of public-health nursing. Perhaps this was colored by the fact that I had been trained in a nursing school that believed more in home nursing than in hospital nursing, and I always felt that I could teach more by taking care of people than just by talking to them.

The Indians were very susceptible to the sense of touch but not really very susceptible to mere words. A hand on their shoulder got more compliance than talking. Those Indians who were not officially declared "competent" were still wards of the government, and though they had help with the problems of land use and land management, they lived well below what we then considered the subsistence level.

I had done no reading about the Indian Service before I went on the reservation as a worker. Perhaps it was just as well that I did not immerse myself in reports of investigations but learned of the conditions at first hand and only discovered gradually the legal and financial limitations imposed by Congress in the administration of Indian affairs. In general my impression of my co-workers was that they were devoted and worked for the benefit of the Indians as their values and experience led them to interpret conditions. I found very few who were soldiering on the job. There was one man who was crazy about playing the stock market, but he wasted only his own substance; he did not involve the Indians. Curiously, he was part of the educational staff. All his contact with the New York stock market was three to five days late, and even I knew better than to try to double my money that way!

But the doctors and teachers and nonprofessionally trained workers were a conscientious lot. They came from the ranks of decent-living people. Some were limited in their interests, but they were honest workers, few heavy drinkers, no dope addicts, and few neurotic personalities. A sense of humor might preserve one from some errors in judgment, but what was appreciated in a fellow employee was industry, integrity, and horse sense. And the three qualities were worth striving for.

One can easily see that the success of my efforts was bound to be very dependent on the interest and co-operation of the reservation administration. The Superintendent, though he did not know as much about medicine as about school teaching, still thought a Red Cross nurse was bound to be an asset and not a liability to the Indians. Neither he nor I nor the doctor could see our way clear to much preventive or health educational work when there was scarcely an opportunity to take care of the sick. I saw plenty of opportunity to teach better nursing care in the homes.

I well remember a sick baby whose father and mother lived in Wood, thirty miles away from the office. They had driven all that distance to see the Superintendent about some land matter. The baby had diarrhea and was very dehydrated when I went to see her. They were camping in a temporary tent area under some cottonwood trees. It was August, the baby was bottle fed; she looked to be near death's door. The doctor said "No hope," but I asked if I could give her boiled water. The parents would not put her in the hospital, so with medical permission I sat down

33

cross-legged on the ground, held the baby on my knees, and kept the mother from shaking her to see if she was alive.

For four hours I kept the infant's mouth wet with drop after drop of boiled water from a medicine dropper. Now and again she would swallow. I came back after lunch and continued the same treatment until suppertime. Nowadays we could give glucose solution intravenously, but that was not possible. We did not have the glucose anyway, and the parents would not take her to the hospital. The father kept up the treatment during the night—the mother did not believe it would do any good, but because the baby had opened her eyes during the late afternoon, the father was encouraged and willing to keep up the treatment. In the evening we gave it a starch enema. It got some fluid that way, too.

Next morning the baby was definitely better, and the mother was willing to co-operate. I took over for about two hours, and by then the baby was swallowing quite often. It was slow going, but we kept at it the entire second day and night. The third day the infant took two ounces from the bottle, mostly water with some milk mixed in. The fourth day the parents wrapped her up, struck camp, and started back home over the prairie in a Studebaker farm wagon. I met them on the road, fifteen miles from the agency, and they were all smiles.

The baby lived through that time, and I had taught the mother something about nursing care. I felt it was worth the twelve concentrated hours—both to the baby and to my reputation—since the Indian police watched me most of the time and would spread the word. My actions were nothing that I had planned, nor part of any "program," but a need had been met, and in spite of any ideas I might have about a program, I was only working to fill the crying needs of the Indians.

Some mothers were afraid to follow suggestions on care of babies. I remember one baby who had bad diarrhea with vomiting, and I wanted to give it a starch enema. The father and uncle wanted me to do it, but the mother was ready to fight with her husband. It was their first baby. Finally, the uncle put the mother out of the hut and held the door while the father held the baby and I gave the starch enema. When I came away, I saw the mother walking over the hills to her mother's house. When the baby recovered, the mother returned home, and when next I saw the couple, she smiled shyly when I asked if the baby was well.

My experience at the Infant Hospital in Boston (for babies under two) had filled me with more authority than I would now feel. Such is youth.

I had done lots of home-visiting nursing in Waltham and Boston. This was really the forerunner of public-health nursing. At Rosebud I felt the Indians needed just as much nursing care as they did medical diagnosis without means of treatment, which was the sad picture of the medical service. The doctor was a good enough sort, overwhelmed by the multitude of calls for which he had no adequate means of treatment. I was not a nurse of the Indian Service but a Red Cross nurse on loan to the Indian Service, hence the doctor could advise me, but he felt no responsibility for making my work a success.

There were twenty beds in a hospital built for forty beds, but the windows on the top floor were so full of crevices and cracks that in a high wind the concrete floor would be covered by drifts of snow, and there was salary for only one nurse. Even forty years ago graduate nurses

35

did not enjoy taking responsibility day and night, week in and week out. Congress had authorized ninety-two such positions at eight hundred dollars a year, but nurses in general would not put up with such conditions of work for long. Generally speaking, the twenty beds were filled with obstetrics, fractures or wounds requiring surgery, and a few old people who needed shelter and food. All the ambulatory patients ate in the dining room along with the employees. The hospital was relatively clean, but many nursing techniques were honored by their absence. Of course, the obstetrical care was better than at home.

VI

Medical Care for Indians

LET ME DESCRIBE the medical and hospital service as I found it on the Rosebud. There were two full-time doctor positions and one contract doctor who made calls down in Winner at the extreme eastern end of the reservation. Only one of the full-time positions was filled; the other had been vacant for some six years. So when I arrived, there was one doctor to take care of about five thousand Indians in their homes and to run the twenty-bed hospital at the agency. He was worked to a frazzle.

It took me some time to decipher the policies that governed the medical service as I found it in 1922. It was apparent to me even then that the two policies—hospital service and home service—were woefully inadequate. The field doctor (we didn't have one) was supposed to tend to the home calls; the hospital doctor was supposed to look after those Indians who would accept hospital care. As I have mentioned, the hospital had twenty beds on the first floor. There was no X ray. There was an operating room and a sterilizer for dressings, which was not invariably efficient, and a dining room for ambulatory cases. The Indians didn't understand the reason for isolation and liked to spend the time chatting with each other. As tuberculosis was the major cause of death, no health service could ignore the problem, but to deal effectively with it was impossible.

The general theory was that the Indians would ultimately all die of epidemic diseases—tuberculosis, measles, and whooping cough in particular. The Indians, however, *did* know that there was a difference between the care in the Rosebud hospital and the "outside hospitals." Many had been to St. Joseph's at Omaha for general surgery and eye operations. A few had been up to Pierre, South Dakota, to be cared for by Dr. Theodore Riggs, the son of an early missionary to the Sioux in Minnesota. Dr. Riggs was a good surgeon and spoke Sioux quite fluently.

Almost all the Indians liked surgery. They enjoyed the drama of "the knife" and really understood the need of cutting some things out; they also loved the X-ray pictures. Of course, we did not have an X-ray machine, but they had had experiences in other places. It was no trouble to persuade them to go to the hospital for surgery, provided it was not the Indian Service hospital. This attitude led up to my taking various cases to Omaha or to Pierre.

Along the lines of preventive work was a policy of examining the school children for chronic and contagious diseases, especially tuberculosis. The doctor did this and gave the immunization for smallpox and diphtheria during the summer. Trachoma was also prevalent, or perhaps conjunctivitis with corneal ulcer.

Children showing signs of active tuberculosis infection were excused from attending school. I suppose as many as one-third of the children were excused. All this responsibility fell upon the doctor, and he worked in the dark— no patch tests and no X ray were available for diagnosis. The stethoscope, the family history, and the general appearance were his guides. Swollen glands were prevalent, though possibly not caused by tuberculosis. It was a sorry picture. One could not blame the doctor or the Indians; the fault lay at the door of Congress and the Indian Office which set down the policies. "No funds" was the answer to any scheme for radical improvements.

I liked the doctor and his wife, but they did not know what to make of me. They could think of many better ways of improving the health service than public-health nursing —and so could I! But as we had no congressional influence, we did the best we could with what we had.

The obstetric service was good; the Indian women liked to come to the hospital. It was a two-week period of rest and social life for the mother, and it provided a reasonable regularity for the babies. At least there was plenty of food and warmth, which was more than there might be at home, where the new mother was usually parked in a tent back of the log hut for a month, winter or summer, with only a pallet on the ground.

The care of wounds and infections was adequate if the Indians would stay in the hospital. They often left against advice.

I had a funny experience on my first trip to take patients away from the reservation for treatment of eye cases. We went to Omaha, where Dr. Charles Gifford was still practicing. He liked Indians and had operated on the Indian chief whose bas-relief adorned our nickel for many years. Dr. Gifford did not make any charge.

My four patients were Mr. and Mrs. Clarence Standing-Bear, Mrs. Jumping-Elk, and Mollie Runs-Reckless. We took the night train to Omaha, sitting up, of course. Directly upon arrival, we went to the doctor's office, where he made the examinations and outlined treatment. Standing-Bear had pterygium, a frequent eye condition among the Indians, which I had never seen before. The wind, sand, and dust seems to stimulate a protective growth of muscle tissue at both corners of the eye, often almost covering the cornea, and sometimes growing right over the pupil,

39

causing blindness. He was to be operated on the next day. Mrs. Standing-Bear got a prescription for glasses; Mrs. Jumping-Elk had glaucoma, and nothing could be done for her. Mollie Runs-Reckless had trachoma, but she refused treatment. The real reason that she wanted to get to Omaha was that she had a boy friend there. Apparently by chance, he was in the vestibule as we came out of the office building. Love will find a way, and they gave me the slip walking from the doctor's office to a taxi. The rest of us had to find a place to stay for three days.

The first hotel where we went would not accept Indians but suggested the name of a small downtown hostelry. We found it. It was clean, had no private baths, but the rooms contained rag rugs and iron bedsteads. I wanted to stay with a friend of my sister-in-law, but without Mollie Runs-Reckless, Mrs. Jumping-Elk was left to room alone. She refused to stay in a single room because she did not trust Mr. Standing-Bear, so finally I left all three in one room in a double bed. I returned at 7 A.M.

Dr. Gifford did the pterygium in his office the next day and wanted to make sure there was no infection. I watched the operation with considerable trepidation since it was done with local anaesthesia and the patient had to co-operate. Fortunately, he understood English well, having been a pupil at Hampton Institute in Virginia. Dear old Dr. Gifford was quite tremulous until his knife touched the tissue, and then his touch was steady and sure. There was little bleeding.

In two days we went back home with two new pairs of glasses for the Standing-Bears, nothing for Mrs. Jumping-Elk, and minus Mollie Runs-Reckless. Superintendent Mc-Gregor laughed at my embarrassment as a chaperone but assured me that I would learn. I did. My respect for the

Indian grapevine increased; Mollie Runs-Reckless turned up about one month later.

This trip set up a great precedent, and I came to be a potential taxi service. Usually I could dig up an alibi rather than refuse point blank. I took Indians off the reservation only when it was arranged by the doctor and the superintendent, but since the reservation extended one hundred miles—from Gregory, South Dakota, to Rosebud—I could have been kept busy just carting people to visit their relatives. This I didn't do, but it was a temptation to see more of the Indians and let the will-o'-the-wisp of public-health nursing go down the drain.

VII

Group Teaching

THE ONLY INDIAN ORGANIZATION was for the men, and I was still looking for some way to teach groups of women. The tribal council, all the older leaders, were given an opportunity to vent their feelings and have a big get-to-gether four times a year. Usually they made their own agenda, and the superintendent gave them some guidance concerning what to discuss. Any man younger than fifty was the laughing stock if he presumed to speak. The biggest subject was the claim of the Sioux against the government for the value of the Homestake Gold Mine up in the Black Hills. They wanted several million dollars, and every phase of the subject was covered by the older spokesmen.

While the men were thus occupied for three days, the women were hanging around, waiting and talking. Finally, Mrs. McClosky, who was one-fourth Indian, was given permission by Mr. McGregor to organize the women. She got them interested in having their own meetings. The organization was called "The Motherhood League," non-denominational, and educational. I was asked to speak to them—not about motherhood, but about my experience in France. There had been many Sioux Indians in France, where they were often very useful as messengers because the Germans could not understand Sioux. They got the message through, and they were also excellent scouts on the front line.

We had one "Motherhood" meeting in the jail. On the top floor was a large room with a few benches, but mostly the audience sat on the floor. Only about half of them understood English, so Mrs. McClosky interpreted. It was my first experience of a group meeting with only Indian women. The polite way for an Indian woman to listen was to bow her head and sit motionless with her feet out in front of her, and all the speaker could see was the parting of her black hair. You have no idea how disconcerting it is to make a speech to fifty black scalps. I used an old speech from Chautauqua, and they listened without a single restless movement. There were quite a few babies and toddlers in the audience, but no Indian is distracted by children. The children are not scolded, nor do they require much watching; they are never noisy or querulous.

I remember ending the speech with a comparison of fighting germs now instead of Germans. We could conquer both. At that point, a very old woman gave the "victory cry," clapping her hand on her mouth. The younger women smiled and told me this was the proper thing for the older women to do whenever a vanquished enemy was mentioned. After the meeting, they served refreshments of cold cornstarch soup—almost pudding, with pounded chokecherry, seeds and all—and coffee. We used the jail plates, but all the women had brought their own tin cups and spoons. I had not been forewarned, so I had to lick my soup from the plate without benefit of spoon.

The second time I talked to them was at Norris, and on this occasion there was a quasi-judicial aspect to the meeting. I've never seen anything quite like it. A young couple were having trouble; they had one child, a young

43

baby. They came before the "Motherhood League" to tell their troubles and get advice. The Sioux Indians, like many other tribes, have the custom of a man never speaking to his mother-in-law. This boy complained that his wife would not live away from her mother, which left him out of all family decisions. A woman does talk to her husband's mother and father, but there is a great deal of difficulty. This couple had no home of their own and were living with the wife's mother. Complaints were heard from both man and wife (in Sioux), and the Motherhood League appointed a judicial committee of three older women to render judgment. All this took place in open meeting. Of course, I could not understand most of what was said, but the final advice was: "Try once more to live together in the wife's home. If it becomes too hard to get along, then move in with the husband's family, but do not break up the marriage yet." The mother-in-law was given a chance to speak also. To me it was very interesting—a public airing of a private family situation. Apparently it worked out quite well, though I don't know how long it worked.

I hoped that Mr. McGregor, the superintendent, would find some way to get a separate home arranged for the young couple. I felt sorry for the boy who could not speak to his mother-in-law but had to live in the same one-room house with her. It must have been hard for him if the girl was under her mother's thumb.

Often young couples gave their first child to the grandparents to raise, to appease the grandmother for having nothing to love. There were many things I never understood about family life among them, but I enjoyed the way they brought up the little children and took care of the babies.

Most of the babies were wrapped in little cotton quilted blankets, very tight and warm. They were taken out of the wrappings about twice each day and allowed to kick on a bed. I thought it a good plan for them to be securely wrapped when they were traveling in a jolting wagon for many hours. There were no cribs and no baby carriages; in lieu of a crib, the babies usually swung in a homemade hammock from the rafters of the log house. Normally they were breast fed on demand. If they were on a bottle, it was condensed milk diluted, not with *boiled* water, and with granulated sugar added. The bottles were hard to keep clean and left much to be desired. I preached breast feeding hard and often.

That reminds me of one compliment I received from an Indian woman. I had spoken at some meeting of women. Since Indians are most ceremonious, after the meeting it was only polite for the audience to come up and shake hands with the speaker. One by one they filed past me; those who spoke no English just said, "Hun," meaning "Good." Those who spoke English usually said "Thank you," but one woman said, "Thank you; I sure do like your preaching." As my father was a Congregationalist minister, I thought how much he would have enjoyed that comment!

VIII

Employees

DEPARTING FROM THE SUBJECT of health conditions which were found, I would like to try to convey some idea of Superintendent James H. McGregor. He was a Hoosier of Scotch ancestry who had dropped the "Mac" in his name and assumed the Irish "Mc." We claimed distant kinship because my MacGregor ancestors had dropped the "Mac" and the "or" to become Gregg and had gone to Ireland when a price was put on all MacGregors at the time of their cattle-stealing activities. Mr. McGregor was a short, rotund man who enjoyed his biscuits and gravy; he was kind and understanding and really liked the Indians. When he retired, he wrote a book of ballads about them, so he had his poetic enjoyments as well as his hardheaded idealisms. He was trained as a teacher and had married a teacher. She was of a thin, wiry physique, and they had three children, a boy and two little girls.

They lived in the largest house, much bigger than they needed, but it was right and proper for the superintendent to have the best dwelling, though Mrs. McGregor hated all the extra cleaning that she had to do. She was a prideful home keeper and always had clean windows, clean curtains, clean floors, and clean dishes. I never saw such meticulous dishwashing—first rinsing in cool water, then hot soap suds, then boiling hot rinse water, then air drying. No drying with tea towels. The sweeping was equally meticulous—and foreign to me. First wet mopping, then sweeping, then a sort of dry rinse with a cleaner mop. All this was because of the dust in summer and mud in winter. The floors were varnished twice a year. Mrs. Mac made Mr. Mac change his clothes when he got home before playing with the children because there were so many sick Indians coming to see Mr. Mac that his wife's respect for germs reached prodigious heights. I enjoyed the friendly contact with his family. The children were bright and gay, with the parents devoted to them and to each other. He was very patriotic and proud of having a Red Cross nurse on the reservation. Although he did all he could to pave the way for me to function, he did not know much about public-health nursing. He did try to keep the reservation sanitary conditions up to the regulations, and often higher than the regulations. He tried to see that each family had window screens and an outdoor privy; he called on each family about once in two years and often took me with him to check the sanitary conditions. He made an official report on these visits to the Washington office. This sanitary check-up was a part of my program for about two months in the fall—I saw a lot of the living conditions in this way.

I especially remember one visit we made to an old, old woman living down near the White River in a log hut. She had no relatives. Her name, translated from Sioux, was "Gets-Mad-Old-Plum." She was nearly blind and lived on government rations taken to her by the native policeman or the farm agent once a month. These rations included flour, lard, cornmeal, oatmeal, rice, coffee, sugar, and bacon, beef, or pork. The original treaty with the Sioux had agreed that if the Indians would stay on the reservation, the government would feed and clothe them "as long as the rivers ran and the winds blew." A later Congress, however, had

47

abrogated that poetic verbiage and given each Indian 640 acres of land, some good grazing land and some worthless.

The Sioux loved their horses and cattle, and they counted their prestige in horseflesh rather than in money. They enjoyed eating beef, but one of the real treats was stew made from dog meat. They made jerky out of beef dried on the clothesline or on barbed-wire fences.

The government idea was to promote a cattle industry, but it was a constant temptation to kill the young steers; to do this they were supposed to have permission from the farm agent, but they were often too hungry to wait for such permission. Their source of cash was leasing the pastures to white ranchers, for which the money was deposited by the rancher at the office. In order to draw on their account, the Indians had to make a trip to the agency headquarters, which made a lot of bookkeeping and much traveling, but it kept the ranchers in line as well as making the money go further.

The social life at the agency headquarters was meager. After a day outdoors I was glad to hole-in and read or write letters and get to bed early. Sociability among the young married employees was confined to having supper together and playing pinochle. Occasionally I was included. Card games were officially frowned on, but there was no other occupation to pass the evening except talking about each other or about our work. Radio had been discovered, but we had no receiving instruments, and there was no sending station nearer than Minneapolis.

No cocktail parties and no dancing parties were thought of—magazines were not prevalent. There was no public library, so books were few and far between.

There were also Indian employees, mostly yard hands, laborers, and policemen, but there was very little fraternizing with them.

48

Mr. Coe was the chief clerk, and he was in command when the superintendent was away. He was a quiet, rather gray little man. His wife was pleasant, also quiet. They didn't mingle much socially, weren't gossipy, and lived plainly. There were two financial clerks, Mr. Cross and Mrs. Davis, whose spouses were also employed. Mrs. Cross was a clerk who did stenographic work for Mr. McGregor. Mr. Davis was the farmer for the agency district—he supervised the farming and land-usage activities. Mr. Manion was the day-school supervisor. He was a strange creature— thought he was a Lothario but was easily squelched. His wife worked at the boarding school. The garage mechanic was George Andrews. He had been a jockey and was now just a little too heavy for a jockey so had turned mechanic. I liked George, and he certainly kept the cars going remarkably well, considering their age and the limited funds that were available. The engineer was a temporary laborer.

I did not have too much occasion for being dependent on any of these co-workers, but I found them agreeable and likable enough. The chief of police was Mr. Rogers, a rather fierce and piercing man. He carried a gun, and it was said that he could use it "very handy." Mrs. Rogers was a very shy Indian woman.

If I had not had my own transportation, I would have had to depend on some of these people to carry me about. I was very glad to have my own car and not be dependent for transportation.

49

IX

Indian Ways

THE INDIANS USUALLY HAD TWO MEALS A DAY—breakfast of coffee and fried bread, and another meal about four or five o'clock in the afternoon. They collected and dried chokecherries and buffalo berries, made peppermint tea, and gathered many wild foods and medicinal herbs. Of course, this type of living was rapidly passing, and they lived to some extent on the type of food they could afford to buy at the store, such as flour, sugar, lard, and coffee. They raised patches of corn, squash, and beans, which they dried and hung from the rafters in flour sacks.

One of the very real problems was the "give-away." A widow would save and starve, sometimes for ten years, to collect enough to have a feast and give-away in honor of her dead husband. She would invite all her neighbors for stew, perhaps barbecued dog and/or beef, and fried bread. Then some friend of her husband would sing a song of praise about the deceased, and she would give the singer her choicest blanket, which would start the ball rolling. Often the give-away lasted three days, and the end result would be a widow with the house stripped bare of equipment, including the kitchen stove.

The medical aspects of these feasts was acute indigestion. I always carried a stomach tube, because their stomachs would be so full and fermented that they had gastric pain, with the gastric flatus pressed against the heart through the diaphragm. They bellowed like bulls in pain, to be heard for a mile or two. I remember one occasion when Miss Groves, the Washington supervisor of home economics, was visiting with me and we came across such a case. The one-room log hut was on an isolated hilltop, with a branch shelter outside the hut. A group of women were clustered around an old man, trying to ease his pain by changing his position. The old man was in agony. He could not vomit.

While Miss Groves wandered around the place, I got out my stomach pump and let out the gas, pumped out a mass of food, and left the old man relatively comfortable—with a weak pulse but nearly normal. It was a good demonstration of the kind of food problem that was not found in the arts of homemaking as included in collegiate home-economics courses.

We went on to the next log house, where there was a new baby. The grandmother was changing the baby, and the navel was dressed with a slice of dried puffball. There must have been either an antibiotic or some astringent substance that dried the cord, as I never saw an infected navel. It was the grandmother's job to have some dried puffballs ready; she also collected bulrushes, and the baby was slipped into a leather bag full of bulrush fluff, which was removed and replaced by fresh fluff when it got wet or soiled. Finally the baby was bundled up tightly in small patchwork quilts. Usually it wore a store-bought shirt and was washed only once in a while. There were few babies who looked neglected.

The cabins were made of cottonwood logs, which harbor bedbugs gloriously. If the babies' skins were spotty, it was usually from bedbug bites. The mothers loved to get olive

51

oil at the hospital (failing olive oil, castor oil or cod-liver oil) to use on the skin. Incidentally, oil was good for making nice, soft buckskin.

They liked and used store-bought soap for their clothing. Of course, the adults washed their lovely black hair in yucca roots dried out and pounded into powder and made into a soap-substitute solution. It worked very well. There were so many valuable medicinal herbs known to certain old women that it was only reasonable to avoid urging remedies that they could not afford to buy and that the hospital could not supply in necessary quantities. It was hard to know what "policies" to follow and where to begin urging "white" techniques.

I remember my own public-health nursing course of study at Simmons College at Boston, where we were urged to teach the poor mothers not to buy canned tomatoes because they did not furnish calories, but that was before vitamins were discovered. Two years later we were told to recommend canned tomato juice for the vitamin supplementary content that all babies should have. Cod-liver oil was known to be good, but no one knew just why. Vitamins A and D were probably in good supply from the sunshine.

The Indians were not good dairymen; they hated to milk a cow. They loved the raw fat from a steer, as well as raw liver and blood from fresh-killed beef; they saved the brains to tan hides but ate all the innards with relish.

All the employees, to the contrary, liked their beef cooked gray. I never had a piece of pink beef until I moved into my little cottage after the first six months. I had been living in a room with a soft-coal stove for heat where I could only make a cup of coffee or some tea before bedtime.

X

Pine Ridge

THE TERRITORY TO WHICH I WAS ASSIGNED was two contiguous reservations, Rosebud and Pine Ridge. After being on the Rosebud for six months, I went over to the Pine Ridge, of which Mr. Henry Tidwell was superintendent. There were no field matrons here; the doctor was not a regular appointee but a temporary one, who was hired while the service was waiting for a regular Civil Service appointee. There was also a contract physician who had a private practice among the ranchers. These ranchers had bought their lands from the Indians, who were given permission to sell by the Indian Office under the provisions of the Dawes Act of 1888.

I found conditions on the Pine Ridge a little less primitive than on the Rosebud. Mr. Tidwell was more of an old-time administrator and less of an educator than Mr. McGregor, who was kindness and understanding personified. Mr. Tidwell was more politically minded and more interested in the economic development of the reservation. I think he was just and possessed high principles, but he was not as interested in my activities as Mr. McGregor had been.

In checking all the children in school, I found so many bad tonsils that Mr. Tidwell asked the Indian Office to send one of the traveling eye, nose, and throat specialists to the reservation boarding school. There was no hospital on the Pine Ridge except a ten-bed affair for sick boarding-school children, with a practical nurse who had had one year of training. The specialist, Dr. L. L. Culp, arrived with his wife, who was also his nurse. I enjoyed them both. He was a typical surgeon—brusque, demanding. He preferred to take out the tonsils with the patient sitting up, so it became my job to hold the younger children on my lap. They were given just enough ether to relax them, and while they were relaxed he quickly snared out the tonsils. He was adept and clever. His nurse administered the ether, and I breathed a great deal of it over the patient's shoulder. After a morning of operating on four cases, we cleaned up and went to lunch, coming back to relieve the practical nurse and see that the children were in good condition and also help with them when they came out of the ether. At the end of two weeks, we had done twenty-five boys and twenty-five girls. Since the little hospital could hold only ten patients at a time, the children were returned to the dormitories in three or four days.

Dr. Culp also checked their eyes for trachoma and put them on treatment—copper sulphate pencil for the worst ones (it burned out the tissue on the lids) and Argyrol for the milder cases of conjunctivitis. When sulphanilimide was discovered, all eye troubles disappeared, and there has been no more copper sulphate pencil-scar tissue for the last twenty years. Of course, sulphanilimide and penicillin have cleared up a lot of infected tonsils.

While the children were recovering, I was troubled about the hospital having no games, books, or toys to amuse them. So I got some water colors, pencils, and paper from the school supplies and set them to making pictures for me; the boys drew rodeo scenes, the girls drew and painted flowers and landscapes. I still have some of those paintings, all cleverly done and well designed.

While it was permissible for the girls to make flower pictures, it was an unwritten school rule that boys were not to draw pictures because it diverted their attention from the more worthwhile pursuits of reading, writing, and 'rithmetic. My intent was not to encouraging subversive activity, but I think the hours spent in drawing pictures endeared me to the children. The heavy-handed attitude of the teachers lasted for many years, but about 1925 Indian art was beginning to be appreciated. The Pueblo artists were starting to do murals under Miss Olive Rush in the Santa Fe, New Mexico, boarding school, and Indian water colors were being sold in New York City for good prices.

With no medical service at Pine Ridge and no general hospital, I could see no sense in the effort to unearth a new lot of health problems. It looked worse than making bricks without straw to me. I did not do much home visiting there, but returned to Rosebud on July 4, 1923, after a two-month stay. I remember that trip vividly, because I made the one-hundred-mile trek across the prairie on a dirt road in four and one-half hours, averaging twenty-five miles an hour. What speed!

XI

Back to Rosebud

THERE WERE ABOUT FOUR MONTHS LEFT in my one-year appointment by the Red Cross, and while I couldn't see any organized public-health nursing service I had accomplished, I had found plenty to do; I had made friends with the Indians and felt useful but still had no scheduled program. On Rosebud I had a house to live in and a clinic room, and I knew I could do very little for either Pine Ridge or Rosebud if I spread my time over the two reservations. The Red Cross put up money for my salary the second year.

In September the government gave permission for a huge Indian powwow to discuss the Sioux claim against the government for seven million dollars in payment for the Homestake Gold Mine (land ceded by the Indians before gold was known). The Indians hired a lawyer to bring their case before the Court of Claims in Washington. There must have been two thousand Indians of the Sioux tribe encamped not far from Rosebud. Most of the tents were the conventional square variety, but any chief with an old-fashioned wigwam or tipi brought it. The plain was dotted with hundreds of tents and campfires, wagons, and horses. The old men held meetings, while the young men who were not allowed to talk amused themselves with horse races and rodeo stunts; the women cooked stews in iron pots, fried bread, and brewed peppermint tea or government-issue green coffee (about half-roasted) over the campfire. They ate beef and chicken and dog, or rather puppies about eight weeks old—a real delicacy. I tasted one mouthful of puppy stew, which was something like bear meat, sweetish but not very appetizing to me—somehow I did not quite like the idea.

Mr. Frederick Leupp, commissioner of Indian affairs under Theodore Roosevelt, had promulgated the theory that the Sioux Indians could become good cattlemen, so Congress had allowed funds to buy cattle for breeding stock. The favorite type of beef cattle was the shorthorned white-faced Hereford, a tribal herd of which lived on the unfenced prairie. This provided meat for the government ration issue, but when I was there in 1922 the tribal-herd idea had been abandoned, and individuals were given some breeding stock. The land had been fenced, and the Indians were supposed to be self-supporting. This government program was to be made effective by the superintendent and farm agents, but it was uphill work. The Indian men loved to ride horseback but were not so keen on keeping their fences repaired. They had been given 640 acres of land—good, bad, or indifferent, some with timber and some without. Even if they worked hard to learn, the cattle rancher's trade did not come easily. To make stationary economic units from a tribal society used to roaming over vast territory was not to be done in a few years.

The tribal herd had been used to supply the twenty pounds of meat issued each month to large families, five pounds to a couple, and less to a single person. The meat was cut, dried on clothes lines or barbed-wire fences, and packed into flour sacks which hung from rafters, later to be pounded almost to a powder for pemmican stew. Beans, squash, and corn were dried and stored in the same way.

57

One very real difficulty in meeting the food problems was that any hungry Indian, on seeing the stored food, would just stay to dinner. The laws of hospitality made it impossible to turn away a guest, so if there was not a secret cache such as a hidden dirt cellar, it was impossible to have food for the family because of the hungry guests. This discouraged many from having food stores on hand. They liked to buy green coffee and roast it in the kitchen oven—it did not taste much like store-bought varieties. Meat was a luxury; fish from the White River and other creeks was not plentiful, and the Sioux ate rabbit fairly often, shot either with a light gun or with a bow and arrow. Sometimes they snared birds, particularly mourning doves. Ducks flew over in migratory seasons. Although there were no game restrictions, they had difficulty in getting the money for guns and ammunition.

The only jobs were government employment, and individual cash came from either leasing or selling land to white ranchers. This was supervised by the superintendent. In the course of time the large allotted tracts of 640 acres were passed on to many children. There was a judiciary department at the agency to settle all inheritance matters.

Old Chief Spotted-Tail had eight wives. His eight-room house, a big square clapboard structure built by the government, stood empty near the agency office. He and seven of his wives and all his children had died. The last wife lived near me with a relative, Mrs. Rubidoux. Mrs. Spotted-Tail was blind, but every morning she climbed the low hill behind our row of houses, faced the east, and chanted a hymn to the rising sun. Her old and quavering voice was true to the quarter intervals that I could never learn to sing or remember exactly.

My friend Jake LaPointe, one of the policemen, used to try to teach me a song about the rabbits to a tune approximating "Turkey in the Straw." I could learn the words but never remembered the tune just right. Jake was the Indian policeman usually assigned to guide me to some distant home difficult to find up some small creek or some little group of log houses beyond the highest bluff off the main traveled trail.

XII

Transportation Lesson

"MAIN TRAVELED TRAIL" was hard to diagnose. Very, very often I was forced to get out of my car to examine the track of the last passer-by. Jake taught me to read the trail according to the way the sand fell from the wheels and in this way to determine which way the last vehicle had been headed. If one asked an Indian the way to He-Dog's camp, it was important to watch the reply as gesticulated. Perhaps by watching what he said with his forefinger, one could take the right road. He usually indicated the main traveled road by pointing forward, his finger describing all the turns in the air. It took me a long time to judge what was the main traveled trail—they all looked alike to me. All were deep wagonwheel ruts. I remember once getting stuck on a high center, with the wheels of my trusty Ford fifteen inches off the ground. I crawled under and chipped out the hard sand and gumbo with my small screw driver.

In the trunk of my car I carried lasso rope strong enough for a 1,200-pound yearling, a trench shovel, a jug of water, a gallon of gasoline, a jack, tire tools, screw driver, wrench, a set of rubber patches for mending inner tubes, my visiting nurse's bag, a hunk of baling wire, and in winter a blanket for the radiator. And don't think I didn't use them. I learned to divine which pair of ruts would go through a forty-foot-wide mud puddle, no telling how deep, and how to wet sand just enough to get traction on a stretch of heavy sand. I have broken the road after a twelve-inch snow; I have spun around on a slick gumbo sidehill that looked too narrow to turn on. One rule was to keep up the momentum at all risks; to stop was fatal.

One of the real compliments I received was from Mr. Presho, the mailman. I had gone to see a woman who was dying of tuberculosis. It was late in March, when the mud was frozen until the sun warmed it about noon. I reached the cabin, twenty miles south of the agency, about nine o'clock in the morning. The family was just barely up, and the house was a fearful mess. I gave the woman a bath, mopped the floor, and generally cleaned up, then cooked some oatmeal. They had killed a calf the day before, and in the front yard was a pail full of entrails and another pail half-full of brains. A cat feasted on the skull. I finished the call a little before noon, having given a demonstration rather than a sermon on cleanliness. On the way home, the frozen mud had melted, and it was only by the grace of God that I got through a long puddle. Then I saw the mail truck behind me, stuck fast in that puddle. I got out my lasso and threw it to Mr. Presho; he hitched it to the bumper, and my little Ford had just enough power to pull him onto dry land. We stayed close together on the way back to the agency. After dinner, I went to the store for my mail, and just as I opened the door I heard this sentence—which I knew referred to me by the ensuing silence—"She's as good as any Goddam man!" Quite an accolade from a South Dakota truck driver.

I can remember many road experiences that were part of the day's work, but a far cry from public-health nursing. There was the time my battery fell out and I ran on the magneto for thirty miles in the moonlight. Part of the way I was behind another car with headlights, but I was in the dark and dared not get too close, yet needed all the light possible. I was glad to arrive home safely that night.

Another time I went down to see a sick Indian near St. Francis, ten miles south. It was snowing, and there was a high wind. Mr. McGregor sent Jake LaPointe with me because it looked like a bad storm. By the time we started home, the storm was fierce, and Jake said we had better find a place to spend the night rather than go on in the blizzard. He knew a family nearby, and we just made it to their yard—visibility eight inches. The farmer had strung a rope from the kitchen door to the barn, a distance of about ten feet, so he could be sure of getting out in the morning if the storm were still raging. This rope gave us support getting in. They fed us, and I slept on the couch, while Jake slept on the floor. The storm was over in the morning, but the drifts were colossal. We shoveled and drove for three hours, getting back to the agency about 10 A.M. Mr. McGregor was relieved to see us and to learn that we had spent s snug night. I doubt I would have had sense enough to stop for shelter, but Jake knew better than to risk spending a night in some ditch.

Another memorable day was in August, about 110 degrees in the shade. No one had told me to let hot air out of the tires. They became very hot, the air expanded, and during that half-day I had ten blowouts. It was no joke. At the tenth, I sat on the running board and bawled with rage and despair. In those days there was no such thing as a spare wheel. The shoe had to be pried from the rim, the inner tube repaired and pumped half-full of air, put back on with the tire tools, and finally filled with air by way of a hand pump. All this was considerable exertion in the broiling sun. For the first time in nine months, I asked myself, "Why am I here?" It looked like an uphill fight with no goal. The courage of ignorance was ebbing away.

62

I remember another trip when my car was stuck in the sand on White River. Mr. Knife had a bad skin condition, diagnosed as lupus, which was thought to be caused by a germ closely akin to that which causes tuberculosis. He used quantities of bismuth subnitrate salve. Mr. McGregor wanted me to visit him and his wife, see what the conditions of the home were like, and take them a check for groceries. So I drove to the edge of the bluff and decided that discretion was better than pride—that I had better walk even though it was hot and the hill long and sandy. Upon reaching the river, I could see the cabin across in a grove of trees. There was a fording place and also a heavy thirty-foot pine log across the swift stream. Water at the ford was also swift, and I didn't know how deep. So I decided to try the pine log although I had always hated plank foot-bridges. There was a loose-hanging guide wire along one side of the log. I carried my nursing bag and was petrified about keeping my balance ten feet above that swiftly flowing water. Hanging to the wire was worse than walking without its wobbly support, but I finally got across.

I gave Mr. Knife his check and dressed his sores, and when he asked his daughter to go for groceries I was delighted, for this gave me a chance to get back to my car without crossing the log. Maria Knife hitched up the wagon, and with her and her little sister, I climbed aboard. It was my first ride in a Studebaker wagon with a loose seat. The horses were quite indifferent, and the moment we got out of the water the road rose in a sharp, sandy slope. Maria stood up suddenly to urge the horses, and the little sister and I turned back somersaults on to the wagonbed, and I found myself hanging with my feet in the water. Maria thought it very funny, and I could see she would enjoy telling the joke on me for not knowing how to balance on a loose wagon seat while going up a steep hill. Indians always enjoyed physical discomfiture, especially of other people, though they will laugh at themselves, too. Anyway, wet feet were much more to be desired than crossing that thirty-foot log again.

In November, Mr. McGregor asked if I would take two very sick Indians to Pierre for surgery. Jake LaPointe and I would be the drivers of two cars, with the patients lying on the back seats. Pete Schweigmann, the chief of police, had been hemorrhaging from a gastric ulcer for six weeks and had at last consented to surgery; Annie Broken-Bow had peritonitis from a ruptured tubal pregnancy. They were well bundled in blankets and pillows. The extra front seat of each car was occupied by an ambulatory case—one a toxic goiter and one a double chronic mastoid. All were running temperatures, and the sick ones had bad pulses. I had my syringe with me in case hypos were needed. We started out about eight-thirty in the morning and made the first sixty miles in four hours. We stopped for hot soup in White River and then went on, hoping to get to Ft. Pierre and the ferry across the Missouri River before 5 P.M. The road was frozen, with rough ruts, and the two cars became separated because of the checkerboard road sections. I was in front, but I turned east while Jake proceeded north for another checkerboard section before turning east and north again. While I was in the first easterly section, I felt a worse jolt than usual and found to my surprise that one of my rear tires was rolling ahead of me into the prairie. In hunting for that damned tire, I crawled under a barbed-wire fence, but the tire had disappeared in the tall weeds. I didn't dare spend much time looking for it, because the last ferry left at five o'clock.

Finally I gave up, and we went the last forty miles on the rim, which was pretty rugged for the gastric ulcer. His pulse

64

was bad. I planned to give him a hypo upon reaching the ferry. When we reached Ft. Pierre at five-thirty, Jake was already there, but there was nothing to do but bunk down for the night at the little hotel and get the first morning ferry. I spent the night swinging between my two patients. Pete's pulse was a running threat of 160, and I could find no pulse at all in the girl. They both got morphine and digitalis, while I snatched a little sleep at the foot of Pete's bed. I was afraid to get too comfortable, for fear I might not awake in time. About six o'clock in the morning we all had hot coffee, then bundled up the patients and lifted them into the cars. It was a dark and cold Missouri River which we crossed; the sun was just rising when we pulled into the emergency entrance of the hospital. Those sisters really looked good to me. Dr. Riggs had expected us the evening before. He took one look at Annie Broken-Bow and told the sisters to ready the operating room. I was told afterward that when her abdomen was opened, the pus shot up to the ceiling. Those were the days before blood banks, and although they did give glucose solution, the technique was to shoot it in as fast as possible and then quit. The present technique of drop by drop had not yet been devised. Annie got well, but she was in the hospital for thirteen weeks. Pete (the gastric ulcer) was operated on at three in the afternoon, but he did not make it, and I had to take the sad news home to his wife. The double chronic mastoid got fixed up, as did the toxic goiter. They were both home in about three weeks.

One other trip was useful to me, though I did not know it then. At that time the Commissioner had three advisors who could be sent to various places at government expense to advise and evaluate for him. One of these advisors, Mr. Thomas Roberts, was living in Pierre and wanted to visit the Rosebud, so Mr. McGregor sent me to Pierre with a sick Indian for the hospital and to bring Mr. Roberts back with me. Mr. Roberts was unfamiliar with automobiles, and I knew he was uneasy about making a 110-mile trip in February across the prairie with a woman chauffeur, but by train the trip would have taken three days. So we left Pierre in the morning about eight-thirty, crossed the Missouri River on a ferry, and started for Rosebud. We got to White River about noon—it would be a hard drive to make the remaining sixty miles by nightfall. About ten miles from the agency we had a flat, which meant mending an inner tube at four-thirty in the afternoon when it was cold and getting dark. While I took off the tire, Mr. Roberts looked helplessly on. The inner tube was past repair. "Now what?" he asked. "Well," I said, "we could go in on the rim, or if you'd go to that ranch house a piece back, perhaps they would lend us a 15 by 60 tube."

He thought it would be worth trying, so I told him if they didn't have that size, I could make the next size do in a pinch. Half an hour later he returned with the larger tube, and I struggled with the tire tools and the shoe, finally getting it in place. We took turns pumping it up. We arrived at the agency about an hour later than expected. I did not realize that Mr. Roberts was so impressed by my resource, sagacity, and zeal, or that I was being considered by Mr. Burke, the commissioner of Indian affairs, for the job of first supervisor of nurses in the Indian Service, but I heard later that Mr. Roberts had said I "would do."

XIII

The Second Year

IN OCTOBER, 1923, we got a new field doctor, Dr. O'Bryan. He was given the cottage next to mine. His wife and two children didn't come with him because he needed to work for two months' salary before he could afford to send for them. He didn't know how to drive a car, so I was chosen to teach him how to drive a government Ford. I got acquainted with him right away.

Dr. O'Bryan's experience had been in a lumber camp in Minnesota and as the doctor on the city ambulance in Milwaukee. Both these jobs had given him excellent diagnostic experience, and he had many good qualities. Two peculiarities, however, were self-evident, a repaired cleft palate and habitual profanity. His habit of swearing was not approved by the Indians. He could and did say "Jesus Christ" and "God damn" without meaning anything derogatory by it. It was an integral part of any good expressive sentence, with a lot of "Hell, God," and simple expletives thrown in. As I have said, the Indian Service employees, while not especially religious, were from a non-dancing, nondrinking, nonswearing, noncardplaying, non-smoking background. Some were shocked by Dr. O'Bryan, others were startled, and some disapproved very visibly. I am afraid that I rather enjoyed it.

When Mrs. O'Bryan and the children, eighteen months

old and four years old, arrived in December, it was very evident that there would soon be another little O'Bryan. I asked if Mrs. O'Bryan were going to the hospital to have the baby, and Dr. O'Bryan said, "God no, I delivered the other two, so I guess I can do this one." So I merely said, "Well, when February comes I will be very willing to help anyway I can."

February came and brought a new little girl. Billy, the four-year-old, came at 7 A.M., knocked on my door, and said, "We've got a new baby at our house." We were living in adjacent little clapboard houses of three rooms—kitchen, living room, and bedroom. The rooms were good sized. Their bathroom, like mine, was a Chick Sales; there was a cold-water tap in the kitchen, and the sink drained (when not frozen) through about twelve inches of pipe which stuck out of doors. The house was heated by two coal stoves. The O'Bryans had to make up the kitchen fire every morning, but their other stove was a base burner and would keep overnight with anthracite coal. It was rugged, but harder on Mrs. O'Bryan with three small children than on me. I went in every now and then to see if she needed help, but was not often that Mrs. O'Bryan needed anything. Everyone carried his own load as a matter of course.

One morning, one week after the baby arrived, I was getting dressed when I saw Dr. O'Bryan bound out of their front door as if shot from a gun. He ran over to my house, knocked on the front door, and yelled, "Glegg! Glegg! Come over and help me. There's a horse, a goddam horse in the kitchen, and I can't get him out!" I threw on a coat and ran over to see what it was all about. Sure enough there was a horse, an old plug of a horse, half-way in the kitchen. The stoop outside the kitchen door was about eight inches high and five feet wide. Someone had left the enclosure gate open, and I had heard the horse wandering about during the night. Dr. O'Bryan had left the kitchen room slightly open when he went out to the woodpile and the "Chick Sales," and when he came back he met the rear end of the horse. He had frantically pushed his way in but had no idea how to remove the horse. His wife and the new baby were in bed; the other baby was in her high chair, and the four-year-old was dancing around half-dressed. Fortunately, I could push past the beast and managed to get hold of his nose (he had no halter on). I led him farther into the kitchen and turned him around, his tail sweeping first over the hot kitchen stove, then into the sink, then across the breakfast table, then over the baby's lap, until I got him past the living-room door and headed out the door by which he came in. The doctor, meanwhile, was jumping up and down with excitement, squawking out expletives. I gave the horse a slap on the haunch, and he lumbered off the stoop into the yard.

The doctor's relief was comic. He exclaimed, "Well! You never can tell what you'll use a goddam nurse for." I went home to light my fire, warm up the oatmeal, and get on with the day. Dr. O'Bryan was grateful and had more respect for my capacity thereafter, and his family were friendly enough neighbors.

His medical work did not run to anything more than answering calls—tiresome when the resources for treatment were so limited. It was quite provocative of a *laissez faire* attitude, and there was good reason for getting discouraged.

There were plenty of medicines, such as they were, on hand, but the Indians were not quite up to co-operating except with the simplest medicaments. It was a sorry picture.

Mr. McGregor used to call me "Runs-Reckless," an Indian family name, but the Indians called me "Wico cujawankaiptiosha," Nurse Cross Red, the woman who takes care of the sick, Cross and Red being translated literally.

Along toward spring they wanted to give me a dance and take me into the tribe. So, as it was still too cold outdoors, we had the ceremony in a log community house. My contribution was ten cans of sauerkraut, by request. They supplied the stew. They also wanted to name me officially. They offered me two names to choose from: "The Rosebud of Rosebud" or "The Helper Woman." Since I did not feel much like a rosebud, I chose the more practical "Helper Woman." They were a little disappointed in my choice as they are quite devoted to the wild prairie rose from which the tribe gets its name. It would have made me more a part of the tribe, I think.

XIV

Indian Service Program

THE ATTITUDE OF ALL THE PEOPLE who were interested in Indians, "the Uplifters" so called, was that the government was hopelessly stagnant and even venal. They blamed the Indian Bureau and almost never considered that the Indian Bureau was the appointed organization for carrying out the laws made by Congress. Of course, there were also certain regulations laid down by the secretary of the interior and the commissioner of Indian affairs, both political appointees. But Congress held the purse strings. And making bricks without straw has limits.

The Uplifters felt that any program good for whites should be tried out on the Indians. Every commissioner had his pet plan. Even President Grant had thought that religion would solve the problem of "civilizing the Indians." Put them on a reservation. Keep them exposed to the missionaries, and all would be well. Let the government feed and clothe them, and they would gradually die off. But they did not. They just became wretched "wards of the government."

After it became evident that religion would not solve all the problems, then education was the answer, and three varieties of schools were established: nonreservation boarding schools such as Carlisle, Hampton, and Haskell; reservation boarding schools; and reservation day schools for the children up to the fourth grade.

In the reservation boarding schools the children went to school one-half day and worked the other half day. There were matrons to oversee the work and a farmer and an engineer for the outdoor work with the boys. Most of the food was produced by the school farmer, including beef, milk, pigs, chickens, potatoes, cabbage, corn, hay, and winter-root vegetables. There was some irrigation for the crops, depending on the needs. The girls worked in the kitchen, cleaned the dormitories, and worked in the laundry. The course of study prescribed by the Indian Office went about to the eighth grade.

In my time I saw many and various programs superimposed on the basic Indian field service—home economics, public-health nursing, health education, protective diets, vitamin dietaries, 4–H clubs, and "the anthropological approach." Somehow we missed the Y.M.C.A. and Scouting.

One of the funniest occurrences was when the service got its first information about vitamins. This was by way of a conference to be held at Rosebud by the Education Department of the Indian Bureau in co-operation with the National Child Health Association with headquarters in New York City. This national association was using up the money Mr. Hoover had left over from Belgium operations.

The home-economics supervisor of the Indian Bureau, working without additional funds, was frantically trying to improve the food standard in the boarding schools, which were often spoken of as "Gravy College." She thought the school personnel should be exposed to the most recent discoveries concerning the leafy vegetables. Perhaps then the Indians would learn to eat lettuce and spinach and cabbage, and the terrible monotony of cornbread, beans, and potatoes with gravy could be mitigated. Congress gave

72

them only eleven cents a day per pupil for food in the boarding schools, the theory being that the schools could raise the rest on their farms. This might have been done in Pennsylvania, but South Dakota was a horse of a different color. All this improvement was to be achieved by this School Conference on Health Education.

The school teachers and doctors from North and South Dakota gathered at the Rosebud Reservation in August, one hundred and fifty of them, including wives and young children—quite a crowd. They were housed in the boarding-school dormitories. The toilets and baths were in the basement—not exactly hotel accommodations.

The first error was in the directive sent to Mr. McGregor, who had been told to arrange for a conference on health education. He had never heard of "health education," so very naturally he thought the typists had left out the word "and." Therefore he got doctors and school superintendents to write papers on health *and* on education. And they all came prepared to make talks to each other.

The second mistake was that nobody told the superviser of home economics that the water supply at Rosebud boarding school was polluted—so full of colon bacilli that two wells and two faucets were used, one for drinking water and another for washing water. I was no help to Mr. McGregor. I did not foresee what would happen or even know much about health education as promulgated by home economists. It had not been invented when I went to Simmons College in 1919 at Boston. Nobody had any notion of vitamins; calories, yes, but protective foods, no, excepting a vague connection between lime juice and scurvy and between cod-liver oil and malnutrition in infants.

The big guns came—the school supervisors and top doctors from the Washington office. With them were the supervisor of home economics and the principal speaker, Miss

73

Schermerhorn, of the Health Education Association in New York City. It was hot, about 102 degrees. Mrs. McGregor organized the food services for the conference, and the teachers' wives helped.

Miss Schermerhorn was introduced at the meeting. The program as laid out by Mr. McGregor was abandoned; the papers requested by Mr. McGregor lay fallow in the breast pockets of doctors and school men, and Miss Schermerhorn was given the floor. For three hours she talked about leafy vegetables. The chairs got hard, the heat was intense, and at last we were dismissed for lunch. We came back at 2:00 P.M., and again Miss Schermerhorn spoke for three hours on the vitality of the well-fed (leafy-vegetable) child. She was full of joy and all the positive radiance that could be promulgated that far from the pavements of New York. She was talking to men and women who were trying to feed from sixty to three hundred children on what they could raise with school children's labor on acreage that had insufficient water.

Miss Schermerhorn was a dark-complexioned, pleasant looking woman, simply dressed, but we all felt her New York elegance in comparing her clothes with our own. She had an effective and sentimental way of speaking. We were "hard scrabble" and knew it. Her opening sentence just put on the lid: "We all know what it is to have joy in our hearts." It was a sketch, to say the least. The joy of raising leafy vegetables without water, for children who were unaccustomed to lettuce, cabbage, or spinach. The children might like carrots, but Miss Schermerhorn said over and over "you can't count carrots." Cabbage was the only possibility to raise, and the Indian children were not enthusiastic about that either. At 5:00 P.M. the meeting disbanded, Miss Schermerhorn exhausted and "the employees" sore in mind

74

and bottom. There was meat loaf for supper and no evening meeting.

At two in the morning I was awakened by the medical director from Washington. He said, "Miss Gregg, do you know where the Epsom salts are kept?" I thought I did and hustled into my clothes only to find that the doctor had already used all the Epsom salts in the school cupboard. So I climbed into my trusty Ford and sped the fifteen miles to the agency where I had ten pounds of Epsom salts in my supplies, then back to the boarding school, where the poor men, women, and children were waiting in lines to get to the toilets. The whole group of them had the most terrific intestinal cramps and diarrhea. Epsom salts seemed a rather drastic purge, but they were ready to take anything. I supervised the women and children, and Dr. Stevens handled the men and boys. It was quite a night, and those who felt able to convene at 9:00 A.M. for more "leafy vegetables" were few. I passed a few men standing weakly in the early morning sunlight, and one of them said jocosely, "You can't count carrots." Of course they talked darkly of meat loaf, but Dr. Stevens and I were sure it was the water. Perhaps they had drunk from the washing-water faucet. Anyway, that is the story of how the Indian Service got introduced to vitamins and leafy vegetables. The visiting teachers and doctors were not impressed with "health education" from New York City. What we needed was more money from Congress.

XV

The Washington Office

IN AUGUST, 1924, I received a letter from the Commissioner of Indian Affairs offering me the position of supervisor of Public Health Nursing in the Medical Division of the Indian Bureau at $2,600 a year with $5.00 per diem when away from Washington. This meant living in Washington and doing office work most of the time, with occasional field trips. I thought it over quite carefully for two days, although I was more than ready to say good-by to the transportation problem of Rosebud, South Dakota. I asked Mr. McGregor's advice. He regarded it as a promotion which I should accept. Of course, I knew nothing about the Medical Division in the Indian Bureau, but I had met Dr. Walter Stevens, the assistant medical director, at the Health Education Conference at Rosebud. I found him a very kindly, unpretentious man. He had been in the Indian Service for many years.

I thought I could find other public-health nurses who would be interested in working on Indian reservations if the Indian office was going to establish that type of service. There are a fair number of nurses who enjoy pioneer work. Finding them would be my task.

So I wrote the Commissioner that I would accept the position and then waited for instructions about reporting for duty. A reply came back very promptly telling me to proceed with Dr. Stevens to the Blackfeet Reservation in Montana where there was to be a big "do" in the nature of a trachoma clinic with a Philadelphia ophthalmologist, Dr. Emmett Fox. In conjunction with this was a three-day meeting with the State Federation of Women's Clubs. All this was being staged by Mr. Hugh Campbell, the superintendent at Blackfeet Reservation. The Blackfeet Agency was at Browning, about forty miles from Glacier Park. So I packed up bag and baggage. The Red Cross was going to send a replacement for me just for the Rosebud Reservation. I sold my old Ford runabout to the garage mechanic for fifty dollars. Mr. McGregor had squeezed out funds to buy a new coupe, and the new nurse, Miss Rose Schwab, would use that car.

There were two field matrons at Blackfeet, and I could have a look at their activities too. One was Mrs. Yates, the wife of the doctor, and the other was Mrs. Helms, the wife of the district farmer. The superintendent, Mr. Campbell, was very active in attempting to solve the food problem. The field matrons did a very good job on canning with the Indian women. They had Mr. Campbell's support and encouragement, and of course had transportation because all doctors and farmers had cars.

I visited each of the matrons for two or three days. They were both strong personalities. Their own canned fruits, vegetables, and meats were in good supply. They had to be, because the winters were so severe that often they were house-bound for two or three weeks. Mrs. Yates kept goats in preference to a cow. I lost my heart to the creatures and found that even I could milk them. If the milk was fresh, it had no goaty taste, and even the butter was edible. The cheese was good.

Mr. and Mrs. Helms had a cow and thus milk to give away.

Mr. Campbell was not in the least interested in having nurses instead of his field matrons. The three days spent with the Federation of Women's Clubs in tow with Mr. Campbell was quite a show. About ten carloads of observers covered the reservation and went to all the Indians who had gardens. They had three barbecues, which the Indians managed. Not all the club women enjoyed their food. We ended up at Glacier Park where Indians were hired by the Northern Pacific Railroad to put on dances for the tourists. I had seen plenty of large Indian camps on the Rosebud, so that was not quite so thrilling to me. Mr. Campbell was a very good publicity man, and he gave the Federated women a big outing. They were enthusiastic and felt that their Indian program was really having some effect on the Indian Bureau. They were doing *good*. I was an observer, not a speaker. It was all very jolly.

The medical portion of the conference there was quite an eye opener. Dr. Emmett Fox, the Philadelphia ophthalmologist, was performing surgery at the little twenty-bed hospital. His treatment consisted primarily of scrubbing the inner side of the eyelids with a toothbrush. In advanced cases he removed the cartilaginous plate in the eyelids, making it impossible for the eyelids to open properly. When the scar tissue formed and the patients recovered, they could open their eyes only halfway. The whole technique seemed horrible to me. His surgical technique was far from aseptic. I saw him drop his toothbrush on the floor, pick it up, and go on scrubbing the eyelid. He was teaching the two service doctors, Dr. Fahey and Dr. Yates, how to do it. I knew enough to keep my mouth shut, but when I thought of precautions taken by Dr. Gifford whom I had watched in Omaha, my thoughts were not complimentary.

From Blackfeet, Dr. and Mrs. Stevens and I returned to Washington. I went to the Laura Dodge Hotel for a day or two until I could find a room nearer the office. Within the first two days I went to see an old friend, Mrs. James K. McClintock, whose husband worked at the Red Cross office. She worked for the American Association of University Women on I Street, just between Connecticut Avenue and 16th Street, where rented rooms and meals were available. As it was within walking distance of the Interior Department on F and 17th Streets, I took a room there.

I reported on the third day to the Indian Office, and was introduced to the commissioner, Mr. Charles E. Burke. I was given a desk in the room with a clerk because there was no desk space in the Medical Division. Stenographic service was provided by a central pool. A few of the offices had individual clerks where the mass of correspondence justified full-time clerical service.

The Commissioner ordered that my initials should appear on any letters that referred to nursing or field-matron work, sending letters back for my initials if they did not appear on the letter. This was the first grasp I had of the fact that Mr. Burke really intended that I should be part of the office organization. I was not consulted before a letter was prepared but was at least informed about what went on. The courage to object to the subject matter of the correspondence was another hurdle that I didn't try to take in the first three months. Of course I knew very little about Civil Service requirements.

This new job was also another shot in the dark. Dr. Stevens had been a great help to me on how to make a supervisory visit on the reservation and how to make my official report to the commissioner of Indian affairs. Dr. Stevens was quite stout, with a slow and easy-going manner and a quiet consideration for others. I was lucky to

79

have his guidance before I got to the Washington office. I expect he felt sorry for me as I was very green in the matter of the Indian Service organization. Also, he must have known that Dr. Newberne, the top doctor, was dead set against the Commissioner's plan of having public-health nurses replace his field matrons. The field matrons were not paid out of medical funds but out of a fund called Industrial Work and Care of Timber, a catch-all title. My salary was to come out of that fund also, so that the Medical Division could isolate me if they chose to be obstructive.

Dr. Robert E. Lee Newberne, the medical director, was a gentleman of the old South. He had worked in the Philippines before appointment in the Indian Service and knew that medical work with primitive people was disheartening. He did not think much of the nursing profession. He would rather have a hard-working, mature, practical woman than any "pretty creature in a starched cap and apron, looking for a husband." In spite of his aversion to nurses, he was kindly, and the workers in the Indian Office were fond of him. That he didn't agree with the idea of replacing field matrons with public-health nurses didn't really bother me when I knew what he was trying to do with a very small budget. There were ninety-two so-called hospitals and sanatoria with a budget of only $270,000. The field matrons were supposed to be under Dr. Newberne's directions, but nobody checked up on their programs and personalities. Most of the superintendents ignored them. Poor things, they worked in a vacuum. Unless they were women of strong motivation their work languished. Some were married to the district farmers. A few had derelict Fords for transportation. My task was to replace them by public-health nurses.

Of course, I expected to be part of the Medical Division, but Dr. Newberne didn't want me. So that was the first hurdle I had to get around. The personnel division of the

Washington office had been doing the recruiting of nurses. They realized that to recruit public-health nurses was a new and special problem, and they were more than willing to let me struggle with it.

XVI

Recruiting Nurses

"THE NURSING LEADERS" in Washington were all most kind and cordial to me after I joined the group as director (supervisor) of nursing in the Indian Service. They were: Julia Stimson of the Army Nurse Corps, J. Beatrice Bowman of the Navy Nurse Corps, Mary E. Hickey of the Veterans Hospitals, Clara D. Noyes of the Red Cross, Elizabeth Fox of the Red Cross Public Health Nurses, and Lucy Mimegerode of the U.S. Public Health Service. We had all been through the First World War.

The big struggle was to recruit enough nurses for all these services, and that was to be my struggle, too. They all knew lots more about the organization required to make "The Services" attractive to nursing personnel. Of course, the civilian services had to function through Civil Service, and that, in itself, was quite something, as the requirements had been set up by a Civil Service Board. All this red tape had to be learned by anyone whose job was to get professional personnel.

Lucy Mimegerode really broke me in to the intricacies. A more loyal friend never drew the breath of life. I say this from experience. She was a stout, dynamic person with snow-white hair and plenty of force in her ideas and in her vocabulary. At national nursing conventions her chief entertainment was to sit in the lobby regaling the passing crowd with her pronouncements. She was vivid and some felt, outrageous. Her family was a well-known Virginia family with connections, but she had come up the hard way. She was an early graduate from Bellevue, where nurses were not considered much above the Sairy Gamp tradition.

I remember overhearing two young nurses talking about the notables in the nursing world at a national convention. One said, "That woman in the green uniform, the white-haired one, is Lucy Mimegerode, I think. She's an F. F. V., I think." And the other rejoined, "Oh, before that, I think." I told it to Lucy when I knew her better, and she enjoyed the anecdote to the full. She had built up the Nurse Corps in the Public Health Service, and she was proud of her achievement as well as her Virginian family background. She could be highly proud of both. There was quality and energy in full supply.

She knew both nursing and nurses. If she found that she was dealing with a timid doctor, she did not hesitate to push him to the wall. She was feared, respected, and admired in varying proportions by the Public Health Service. She took me on as a neophyte. Although she could have been scornful of my ignorance, she was generous enough to give me her support and guidance. We had many good times together. We all had our problems, and the solutions varied, but we all needed the same elements of discipline, understanding, and hopes in order to give good care to the patient and loyalty to the medicos.

The Army, Navy, Veterans, and Public Health Service were all medical organizations—patients, doctors, and nurses. I had a fourth factor, the lay reservation superintendent as the top administrative officer. One more headache, one more hurdle.

It was up to me to find nurses for a new government nursing service. I went right on and talked to nurses—

students and graduates—wherever I could get the chance; and nurses were interested and were willing to try. They were intrigued by the adventure of using their knowledge where it was not only needed, but something of a challenge.

Of course the nurses had to get along with whoever was on the job as a doctor, and the doctors had to put up with some nurses whose sense of freedom in the wideopen spaces was off the beaten track. I remember that one field nurse was adversely reported on her probation because she had a family of pet skunks under her kitchen stove. The doctor thought this a poor example of hygiene to the Indians. Incidentally, the Indians were not above eating skunk when rabbits were in short supply.

Take it all together, I laughed more than I cried over all the varied contretemps of the human race. Naturally there were both doctors and nurses who were competent, hard working, wise, and kind. There were others whose foibles were more prominent than their virtues. Yet on the whole there were only a few who solaced themselves with alcohol or narcotics. One only hoped to find their peculiarities before the six months of probation gave them permanent status under Civil Service. There was a general tendency among the superintendents to be lenient in their criteria. The sexual vagaries (both homo and hetero) were ever present, much exaggerated by the isolation and barren social outlets. I often felt rather responsible for the mistakes of the younger nurses, although I always told them in advance how isolated the stations were. But they did not know the hard meaning of the word.

Up in Alaska many is the sweater that has been unraveled so that it could be knit up again as "busy" work in the long dark days, while the Eskimos slept, waiting for the moon to give them light enough to play their football games. Their football was more like a large handball made

84

of sealskin and filled with old cotton from some missionary bed quilt.

I have drifted away from the Indian Office. If I had not had two years on a reservation I would have found the work in the office much more difficult. Just sitting still behind a desk was in itself a trial. About an hour and a half was all I could take, and I welcomed interruptions. That was one reason why I liked to talk over the problems that came into the office via the five mails each day. If the problem involved some other division, I usually wrote a rough draft of a letter and then took it around to see what the other division might have to say. One very soon got over the pride of authorship as all letters had to pass not only through the medical division but also any other divisions involved, then through the personnel and then through the inspection division, to the assistant commissioner and finally to the Commissioner for signature. I became a fluent and polite letter writer.

I give one instance of a nursing-personnel problem that came in to Washington. The reservation superintendent was having difficulty, and he wanted me to come out and straighten it out. The superintendent was new at the job, having been recently promoted from a chief-clerk position. There were three women on his payroll who were quarreling. We will call them Ella, Bella, and Stella. Ella was a nurse, Bella was a school teacher, and Stella was a clerk. Ella and Bella had been bosom friends, but Bella had transferred her affections to Stella. Ella got so mad that she began to carry a gun and threatened Bella and Stella. They were scared and reported it to the superintendent. He, poor man, also took fright and wrote to the Washington office and wanted me to come out and settle Ella, the nurse. Of course the office wouldn't let me go—so I prepared a letter for the Commissioner's signature, telling the worried superintendent just to sit tight and ignore the situation and that it would blow over. It did. The nurse put her gun away and about six months later an opportunity came about to offer her a transfer to her native state, which she accepted. All's well that ends well.

XVII

Protocol and Procedure

WHEN I FIRST WENT INTO THE WASHINGTON OFFICE in September, 1924, I had a great deal to learn. Although I knew a good deal about the protocol of a large hospital, I knew nothing about protocol as it then existed in a large government bureau. Nor did I even know how important and how inflexible the procedures were thought to be. There was a way to do work, and only that way was considered valid.

I will not even try to give a complete outline of the then existing official setup, as all of that can be found in the Meriam Surveys of the Bureau of Indian Affairs done by the Brookings Institute in 1927 and 1928. These monographs not only describe the functions of the bureau but also make some criticisms and recommendations.

One of the strictest rules was that all correspondence must go out over the Commissioner's signature. I could write no letter to the nurses nor they to me. My chief concern was with the Medical Division, where I naturally thought I belonged. When it became evident that the Medical Division intended to bypass me, I knew I was out on a limb. The Commissioner was my ultimate support, but I did not like bypassing the Medical Director and going to the top all the time.

I had to set up qualifications for public-health nurses

within the Civil Service Commission. The Indian Office thought that the title "public-health nurse" would be confused with the Public Health Service, so they decided that nurses who were appointed to do public-health nursing were to be called field nurses. I didn't quite like it but acceded to their wishes. I thought it too closely associated with the title "field matron."

The Personnel Division, which made all Civil Service appointments to the field jobs, was very overburdened with work and was glad to have someone outside the division working on appointments. It had never been able to fill the vacancies set up for Civil Service nurses because nurses interested in government work were more acquainted with the Army and Navy and Veterans Administration and Public Health Service than they were with the Indian Service, and practically all the Civil Service jobs were preempted by the Veterans Administration. The Civil Service didn't hold examinations for nurses. They just listed applicants who met their qualifications and had requested appointment. Of course, the reservation superintendents were allowed to hire nurses "temporarily" if they could recruit them locally. This expedient, however, gave the nurse no security as she had to be replaced by a Civil Service applicant if one could be found. The crux of the difficulty was that the nurses were accustomed to being hired by a director of nursing, and the letters from our personnel division, signed by the commissioner of Indian affairs, did not attract them to these isolated jobs on Indian reservations. I could describe the jobs much more accurately to a nurse than the Personnel Division did. Of course, the major factor for the hospital jobs was the low salary, with long hours of work. There was only one Indian Service hospital that employed two nurses, so all nurses were on call at night.

I wrote an article for the *American Journal of Nursing*

which brought some letters of inquiry. I got permission to answer them over my own signature with "by direction of the Commissioner of Indian Affairs" added. Not many nurses were drawn toward this type of pioneering. Many tried it and gave it up.

The hunt for nurses, both for the hospital jobs and the field-nurse jobs, continued to occupy my time and efforts all that year. I made a good many appointments, but both the doctors and superintendents preferred to hire temporary nurses so that they need not bother with Civil Service regulations. The superintendents could save money by hiring a temporary practical nurse, and the doctors did not always want a trained assistant. It was easier to manage an untrained helper. These attitudes were hard to combat by correspondence.

The conditions of work were hard for a civilian nurse to understand in comparison with the Army, Navy, Veterans, and Public Health Service. The Indian Service offered twenty-four-hour duty, no annual leave, and only eight hundred dollars a year salary for hospital nurses. No wonder the labor turnover was high! After I had been working on appointments for a year, I wanted to take account of my efforts.

After the first year of work I was talking with a friend in the Bureau of Labor Statistics about my difficulties, and she suggested that I do a set of figures on "labor turnover." With her help I prepared a memorandum which I sent upstairs to the Department Personnel Office. I was the first person in the Interior Department to do a labor turnover study. It showed that there had been an 800 per cent turnover of Indian Service nurses on reservations. Mrs. Maulding, chief of the Personnel Division, wondered why. I could tell her, and I did. She was impressed.

I stayed in Washington all that winter. The Personnel

Division wanted me to fill all nurse positions, hospital as well as field (public-health) nurses. This changed the focus of my job. I suppose I filled about fifty positions for hospital nurses on the reservations.

XVIII

The Uplifters

ONE OF THE SURPRISES that I had after a few months in the Indian Office was the number of people given to writing the Commissioner about their objections to the way the Indian Office conducted its affairs. Another surprise was the amount of official advice paid for by the government. First of all was the committee of three commissioners to the Commissioner, all three of the highest caliber, Dr. Samuel Eliot, Mr. Henry Vaux, and Mr. Charles Eastman, each of whom received one dollar a year plus expenses. All were high-minded gentlemen. The Commissioner also had three advisors of his own choosing, who were versed in politics and more conversant with the hard realities of the Congress under whose laws the Commissioner had to operate. The Indian Committee of the Congress was Joe Robinson, chairman, of Arkansas, and five others, mostly from states where the pressure from timber, grazing, or mining operations by white men was strong. There were the executive secretaries of civilian groups, the Indian Rights Association of Philadelphia, and the New Mexico Indian Association. These men were paid by their organizations to travel and evaluate the actual field conditions through whatever colored glasses they chose. They rarely put on rose-colored ones. Also there was the Secretary of the Interior, and often his wife had to be taken into serious consideration.

There were the free-lance anthropologists, too, like Elsie Clews Parsons, and the pseudo-anthropologists such as Mary C. Wheelwright. They were all bent on proving that the Indian Service was either stupid or venal, or both.

Inside of my first six months I was called in to see President Charles William Eliot, of Harvard University, Dr. Samuel Eliot's father, in Cambridge. He asked if I thought money from an ancient English fund which he had to administer, called the Propagation of the Gospel Among the American Indians, could be properly spent on hiring a public-health nurse. I told him that while I thought it would do the Indians lots of good, it wasn't my interpretation of the gospel. He did not make the money available.

At that same time I was called to drink a cup of tea with Miss Mary C. Wheelwright on Beacon Hill. I put on my best bib and tucker and was ushered into the elegant reception room, where I sat waiting for Mary C. Wheelwright for forty-five minutes, getting madder and more bored by her rudeness every minute. When I was just ready to examine all the rich and rare objects of art on the mantelpiece, the redoubtable Mary walked in with a slack apology on her lips and a very elegant maid and tea tray just behind her. She talked for forty-five minutes about the Indian Service, telling me what a fool I was to think I could get any decent nurse to work for Uncle Sam's Indian Service. Fortunately I did not have to say more than "yes," "no," or "It that so?" So I escaped without trying to influence her opinion. She had made up her mind and was thoroughly accustomed to being listened to.

Another encounter that helped me was in New York— lunch with Elsie Clews Parsons and her husband. A very good lunch. She gave me the once-over and forthwith devoted her attention to my escort, Dr. Carl Binger. That left her husband, Henry, to talk with me. Being a politician by profession, he was kind enough to tell me not to expect to arrive at my goal in a straight line but to be content to zigzag in the general direction of my objective in the next ten years. He knew immediately that I had been nurtured in idealism and that the road with opportunism would be thorny. So while I enchanged no views on anthropology with Elsie, I got some practical advice from her husband that I knew was kindly and true.

The net result of these encounters was to make me determined to stick to my knitting—not to dabble in politics but to be content to zigzag in the Bureau of Indian Affairs.

XIX

First Field Trip—The Southwest Pueblos

IN FEBRUARY, MR. BURKE SENT FOR ME and questioned me about my plan of action in setting up the new field-nursing program. I told him that I thought it wiser to leave the present field matrons until I could get public-health nurses interested and willing to undertake work in the Indian field. He told me that I'd have to sell my ideas to the various superintendents and that I had better make a field trip to study the conditions in various parts of the country. There was at that time considerable pressure from the New Mexico Indian Association for a public-health nurse for the Pueblo Indians. So my itinerary was the Northern and Southern Pueblos, the Zuñi, and all six Navaho reservations. This included the Hopi Pueblos on the Keams Canyon Navaho reservation. I figured that it would take at least three months.

In Santa Fe, where the Northern Pueblo Agency had its headquarters and the New Mexico Indian Association operated, I met the superintendent, Mr. Crandall. He was an old-timer just working out the last few months before his retirement at seventy-two years of age. I telephoned to the Secretary of the Indian Association and told her that I would be glad to meet with them. They arranged an evening meeting at the home of Mr. Nordfelt, an Association member. Mr. Crandall did not go with me. I talked about my experience in Rosebud, and about Miss Augustine Stoll, who had been the Red Cross nurse on the Jicarilla Apache Reservation in Dulce, New Mexico. While they were perfectly polite to me, the undercurrent attitude was "Can any good come out of Washington?" They had worked very hard at defeating the Bursum bill and had lumped Mr. Burke, Albert Fall, then secretary of the interior, and the Teapot Dome Scandal together and were perfectly willing to find me part of the same gang. We ended the evening on a more cordial footing, aided and abetted by punch and cookies and my assurance of willing co-operation with them if they established a public-health nurse stationed in Española to serve the Pueblos of San Ildefonso, San Juan, Santa Clara, Nambe, and Tesuque. I have not the slightest recollection of what I said but felt the evening was time well spent.

Later I recruited a nurse in Boston for the New Mexico Indian Association. Miss Hilda George from the Massachusetts General Hospital took the job, and she was stationed at Española, where there was a contract doctor. She was a qualified public-health nurse—gentle, flexible, and determined. She found plenty to do.

I had an unusual experience with Superintendent Crandall. I had more or less insisted that I see and visit all the pueblos, so he drove me down to Santo Domingo. He had an errand with the governor of Santo Domingo, and I tagged along and got a general impression of what was then the largest pueblo. We did not know that particular day was the Domingo counterpart of April Fool's Day.

Their joke was to throw a pail of water over any man who showed up. The women were having a big time. When Mr. Crandall, unsuspecting, turned around the corner into the Plaza, some woman, not seeing who it was and, I suspect, not caring much, threw a whole pail of water in his

95

face. I was walking behind him and only got splashed a little, but Mr. Crandall was drenched. I really admired his aplomb. He didn't get angry, just brushed himself off and went on to the governor's house. There was a lot of giggling behind us and some scowling, but we stayed there about half an hour. I was introduced and explained to the governor. There was no enthusiasm about nurses. The governor said they had medicine women of their own and would not want any white help in that line. Visitors were not welcome.

At the other pueblos the Indians were not exactly unfriendly to white medicine but were noncommital to the idea of public nurses. Measles and diphtheria and whooping cough, tuberculosis, meningitis, and diarrhea were the main causes of death among infants and young children. We had toxin antitoxin (shots for diphtheria) but nothing for whooping cough or measles or other diseases. Now we use DPT to protect from diphtheria and whooping cough, gamma globulin for measles, and BCG for tuberculosis. Of course, there are still colds, flu, diarrhea, and pneumonia but far fewer epidemics that raise the infant death rate to shocking proportions.

Time and the automobile, schools, and the gradual change of Indian Service policies had much to do with the breakdown of resistance born of old cultural attitudes.

No man under fifty was permitted to speak his mind, and that left the young men back from the war with little influence; they had to readjust to life in the close-knit pueblo government. The young women had much less experience, so they continued in their pueblo tradition with a firmer allegiance to the old ways. Their contacts with white life were limited to boarding schools and a few jobs in Santa Fe and Española households.

Of course, there was quite a little drinking. The men

were not then supposed to be able to buy liquor, but there were ways, and the "white mule" of prohibition days was available and potent. The Indians were all members of the Roman Catholic church but retained much of their native religion interwoven with Catholicism.

The pueblo council was made up of a religious leader, who remained in office as long as he lived; the governor, chosen by the pueblo for a term of years (his appointment was ratified by the President of the United States); and several lieutenants to help the governor. This council settled all tribal matters. They approved of marriages, chose the workers for the community work, parceled out the arable land to different families, managed and allotted the irrigation water, and arranged for the care of the widows and orphans. They dealt with the superintendent of the agency on all matters that came from the government, such as roads, water pumps, fences, and tribal funds. The day schools were manned by the Indian Service teachers, and there was usually a "government farmer," now called an extension agent.

I found the two public superintendents dubious concerning the value of a public-health nurse. There were no full-time doctors. The day-school supervisor was not a great help in health problems. However, they were not actually obstructive. The visits turned out to be much more of a survey of the pueblos and the going facilities than a plan to appoint field nurses.

There were infirmaries in connection with the Santa Fe and Albuquerque boarding schools, but they did not serve the adult Indians or young children. There were contract doctors to whom the Indian could go if so inclined, but this phase of medical service was pretty meager. It seemed to me that a nurse could do a home-visiting nursing program, and perhaps school nursing with some emphasis on

97

health education in the pueblos that fed those two schools. Success would depend on the initiative and personality of the nurse.

The geographical setup of the pueblos was such that more than one pueblo could be served by one nurse. The study of geographical and transportation factors was one of the facets to be considered. All this gave me a pretty full impression of the conditions a public-health nurse would have to meet. I don't remember being discouraged about finding nurses, but they didn't come in swarms. I had to hunt for them, and this took time. If I was on a field trip I couldn't do much work on recruiting in Washington, so I had a lot of catching up to do when I went back to headquarters.

Superintendent Crandall was hardheaded and carried out the policies of the Indian Service. The government had no over-all economic plan for the Indians, who really didn't want any hospital care. Sheep and cattle had originally been provided by the government, and they had water pumps from the government and large land grants from Spain. Subsistence farming was practiced with irrigation from the Río Grande. There were usually two factions in each pueblo, progovernment and antigovernment. The most pronounced antigovernment groups were Taos and Santo Domingo, who wanted to be allowed to go their own way. Neither of these two pueblos wanted a day school, and the older children were sent perforce to the Indian boarding school at Santa Fe, which then took first grade through eighth grade. The day schools took the six-year-olds to get them accustomed to school and to begin to teach them English. The boarding schools took the older children who might be only in the first grade but were out of place with six-year-olds.

The women made pottery, and the Museum at Santa Fe

encouraged them and displayed and sold their wares. Mr. Hewitt, then director of the Museum, was particularly persistent in encouraging the Indian women. Especially fine black pottery was made by María Martínez. Her husband, Julian, drew the decorations. The pots and the firing were done by Maria, and Mr. Hewitt created a market for her wares.

There was one outstanding Indian artist, Awatsirah, who painted delightful Indian pictures in water color. His work was exhibited in New York. But at that time no school child was allowed to draw in school. The Indian Office was only interested in having the children learn the three *R*'s. This old policy of the Education Division was finally changed in the 1930's, and the Indian children were encouraged to develop their talents.

From Santa Fe I went down to Albuquerque. The superintendent at Southern Pueblos was Mr. Odle, who didn't care what the Indian Service did about either field matrons or field nurses. He was going to Laguna with the day school supervisor, Mr. Morrison; I could come along if I wanted to. So I went along. A storm came up, and they decided to spend the night. We were given a shakedown. I slept cold and came down with a terrific cold. However, I saw the pueblo, and the next evening they decided to go back to Albuquerque. We left about 5 P.M., expecting to get in for a late supper, but about ten miles out from Laguna we scared a bunch of horses from the ditch by the roadside and ran into one of them. I was lying down on the back seat, and the impact of the horse threw me onto the floor. The horse got his foreleg tangled between the headlight and the hood and was thrown sideways onto the running board. There he sat beside me, the biggest horse I ever saw. As we slowed down he freed his foreleg and rolled off onto the road, but his weight put out the headlight and jammed

99

the radiator into the fan belt. There was the most terrific clatter. The men hopped out and pulled the radiator forward. I was concerned about the horse, but the men said they didn't give a damn about the horse. We limped back to Albuquerque, uncertain about getting there and very late for supper. I was glad to get into a steam-heated room.

Mr. Morrison took me to see several of the pueblos. He was interested at the moment in the sonnet and bet me I couldn't write one. So I produced a sonnet to him. This literary effort is lost to posterity, but Mr. Morrison was pleased with my effort! One never knows what public-health nursing may lead into. However, I returned to my knitting, which was public-health nursing.

I then visited the field matrons at Isleta and Jemez. They were not doing much. The woman at Isleta had a sick husband who took much of her interest and time. She meant well but had little to show me of her work or plan of work.

At Jemez the field matron had been originally hired to try to teach the Indian women lacemaking. A do-gooder had visited the pueblos and had the idea that with so much skill in handwork shown by the Indian women, they could be taught lacemaking, which she had learned in Italy. So the Indian Bureau, dubiously I suspect, allowed her to try it out at Jemez Pueblo. Quite a few Indian women learned the rudiments of making pillow lace, but it never took hold in any economic volume, and the women grew tired of the project. After finding another woman who accepted an appointment as field matron to teach lacemaking, the patroness departed and the field matron took over. At the time of my visit the women were doing pottery, tanning hides, and making moccasins according to the old-time division of labor.

The field matron had abandoned lacemaking and was helping the men who weaved and embroidered the kilts worn by the dancers in the original costumes for the native dances. The men had taught her how to weave the string belts also. The day I visited Jemez, the field matron was busy weaving a string belt. She lived near the pueblo and would also visit the sick if the Indian women wanted her help. She made her own program. Naturally I thought that a public-health nurse would be much more of an asset to the health of the Indians. Mr. Odle didn't care much. Either program suited him if the Indian Office wanted to try it out. So I decided to replace this field matron and the one at Isleta as I could find nurses to undertake it. In two or three years I found two nurses to fill these jobs. One of them lived at Isleta but also visited Santa Ana and Sandia. The nurse at Jemez was paid by the New Mexico Indian Association and also visited Zia. Gradually the Indians came to depend on the nurses, and later field doctors were employed full-time instead of using the contract men from Albuquerque. The program took about five years to really get established.

Neither of the nurses tried to interfere with the native child care of the Indian infants. The babies were on boards. The toddlers were in native costumes, but the Indian mothers were beginning to buy ready-made clothes for them. Rompers became popular for the two-year-olds, then Levis and shirts for the four- and five-year-olds, both boys and girls. When the children went to school, the girls had uniform blue and white drill dresses and the boys, Levis and shirts.

One of the very real problems for the field nurses was not to become a taxi service for every Indian who wanted to get to town. It was hard to turn them down without losing one's influence. I suspect that many a trip was made for other than health reasons. It could not be otherwise in the beginning.

101

XX

First Field Trip Continued—The Navaho

FROM THE PUEBLO AGENCIES of Santa Fe and Albuquerque I went on to Zuñi and the Navaho Agencies. There were at that time six Navaho Agencies: Southern Navaho, at Fort Defiance; Northern Navaho, at Shiprock; Western Navaho, at Kayenta; Eastern Navaho, at Pueblo Bonita; Leupp; and Keams Canyon, which also had the Hopi pueblos.

When I had finished at Albuquerque I went to Zuñi Pueblo, forty miles south of Gallup. I don't recall much about that visit except that I bought a lovely big piece of pottery and two turquoise rings.

Zuñi had a small hospital with a temporary doctor and a temporary nurse. Like all other pueblos, it offered a good opportunity for a public-health nursing service.

When I went from Zuñi to Fort Defiance I found one of the best doctors in the service, Dr. Polk Richards. He was a good surgeon, a hard worker, and took all sorts of risks to give the best individual care for the money available. He had one nurse for a forty-bed hospital. Dr. Richards was especially interested in eye disease. Trachoma was prevalent. He had also one nurse especially trained in eye care. This gave him two nurses in the operating room, one of whom could give the anaesthetics. Although the hospital was officially a boarding-school hospital, for Dr.

Richards it was a general hospital. If the Navahos would come, Dr. Richards took them in, infants and adults as well as the school children.

Dr. Richards was short and stocky and had a quiet, quizzical temperament. He had been working with the Indians for fifteen years, and they trusted him. They had reason to, for he understood them and told them what he thought he could do with their help and co-operation.

His general nurse, Mrs. Showalter (Show for short) was devoted and hard working. She was part Indian and a registered nurse, but not Civil Service. Their sterilizer was an old army field contraption that they had to use outdoors because of its tendency to blow up. When it didn't blow up, it sterilized, but all the sterilized dressings had to be dried in the kitchen oven. It was what might be called a piece of work, to do a batch of dressings, obstetrical packs, etc.

The hospital had cost about fifteen thousand dollars to construct originally. It had two clinic rooms, one on each side of the entrance. Then a wide corridor led to a male ward of twenty beds on the other end. There were toilets attached to each ward. Bed pans were cleaned and disinfected in the bathtubs. There were no separate toilets for the hospital staff.

The patients' dining room was opposite the front door, the kitchen behind that. There was no cart or carriage for the trays; meals were served in the kitchen and carried by hand to the bed patients. The building was a frame fire trap. How they managed was a daily miracle.

The day I visited, there was a conglomeration of cases in the women's ward that shocked my nursing sensibilities. A delirious woman lay on a mattress on the floor because she was afraid of bedsteads. She had an open abscess over the spine, so wide and deep that the vertebrae was laid bare.

103

There was a mother and baby, the mother with puerperal insanity, and in the far corner was a child with diphtheria. Two children with pneumonia following measles were there as well as a newly delivered mother and baby, a typhoid fever case, and a tubercular meningitis baby. Only one nurse and two attendants were present. Needless to say, I couldn't say much about nursing techniques. Cross infections were in the hands of the Lord and the Congress. It was only a little better than the hogan, but with warmth and food and cleanliness, it was the best that could be done. I longed to talk to the Indian Committee of Congress, but I had only respect and admiration for Dr. Richards and Mrs. Showalter. They, however, eyed me with some hostility because I came from Washington "looking for things that were not up to standard hospital practice." Oh, dear, what a long trail ahead of me!

From Fort Defiance I went to Chinle and found a shabby and derelict hospital which was a boarding-school infirmary with a no-account doctor and a stupid practical nurse, then up to Northern Navaho at Shiprock, stopping at Tohatchi, where a new doctor was in the first stages of bewilderment. He was Swedish and not accustomed to a down-at-the-heel "government" facility. This was a ten-bed boarding-school infirmary. A practical nurse was doing her (not very good) best giving eye treatments and taking care of flu cases.

Up at Shiprock there was another rattletrap hospital— a wooden frame structure built as a tuberculosis sanatorium. The one nurse was trying to cope with an epidemic of measles among the school children. She had forty cases, some in the building and some on the porches, which were not glassed in but had only cloth curtains. The hot-water boilers had "gone out," and the poor girl was about at the end of her tether. My sympathies were all for her, and I

104

raised Cain with the superintendent and the weak, ineffective doctor, and in five days the boilers were fixed.

At this visit I was interviewed by two old Navahos who had heard by the grapevine that I was coming, and they had ridden one hundred miles from Bluff, Utah, on horseback, to ask "Washington" to send them a new doctor who "could cut." They had only an internist, Dr. Gillespie. Their own Navaho medicine men could take care of other illnesses, but they had only a piece of glass to cut with, and that was not very successful even with an appendix abscess. They wanted a surgeon, not an internist! The two doctors at Fort Defiance, Dr. Richards and before him Dr. Wigglesworth, were surgeons. The Indians knew the difference. I explained that I would write to the Commissioner in Washington and when I went back there would talk to him as well. It would take time, but perhaps we could find a surgeon for them. They thanked me and rode back home feeling that they had seen an official and had gone through channels.

Around Shiprock I visited several missionary centers. They, too, were trying to make bricks without straw. It was a case of pitiful devotion without adequate support from their mission boards in New York. I, in my mind, was trying to decide upon the best locations for public-health nurses. It would cost more to have nurses in these locations than if they were placed elsewhere. They would have to have a house, a car, and an interpreter-driver. It would be quite an order for Congress to implement, and for me to recruit that kind of nurse, also.

From Shiprock I went by the back road over to Kayenta. It was a "sanatorium school," and the pupils all had tuberculosis. The doctor, originally from Arkansas, was a prestidigitator. He could pull a dollar out of the Indian's nose

105

or ear, a feat which either amused or befuddled the Indians but was not always a joke to them. Kayenta was where the Wetherills had a trading post. Their scorn of the Indian Bureau was easily seen and not very surprising. Lord, what a picture! I visited several trading posts, and for the most part the traders and their wives were kindly. But they were there to trade and not to give away their goods. I got an eyeful and an earful of impressions.

From Kayenta I was driven ninety miles by car to the Hopi-Navaho Reservation headquarters at Keams Canyon. This jurisdiction covered Navaho country and the Hopi villages on three mesas about thirty miles to the south and west of the agency headquarters at Keams Canyon. At two of these villages there were field matrons. Lizzie Donnelly at First Mesa was the best field matron I had encountered. She lived in a very simple adobe house of four rooms, where I stayed with her for a week. She was a keen judge of human nature and a strong influence with her never-ending patience and kindness, a real force for the Indians. She was from Tennessee, I think from the mountain area. She enjoyed her work, and the simplicity and the study of individual character and the mores of the pueblos were a challenge to her. Her white hair and lovely spirit were enjoyed and respected by Indians and whites alike. She didn't let them encroach on her but at the same time was generous. She was a finely balanced woman, who could cook and nurse or console and advise without getting involved or petty when situations got out of hand. She had a clear head, a kind, and a practical hand. After I had seen Miss Donnelly and she had told me that she was a friend of Dr. Newberne from their home town in Tennessee and that she had refused his proposal of marriage, I could understand why Dr. Newberne was so dead set on his field-matron program.

At Second Mesa the field matron was the wife of the

106

school teacher. She was of a jealous disposition and thought very little of a missionary couple who lived nearby. Friction was constant and bitter between them, a poor situation going sour with rapidity.

The Third Mesa was very hostile and unco-operative. The missionary minister preached every Sunday on the plaza. The Indians stayed in their houses, doors and windows shut. This had been going on for fifteen years. The minister's devotion to his calling was worthy, and his church could not acknowledge defeat. His approach was foreign to the Indians and "right" to him. Poor man and poor Indians!

I was very much interested in seeing this group of pueblos. They seemed to be more ancient than the Río Grande villages. Situated as they were in a remote and difficult spot, withdrawn from their old-time enemy, the Navahos, the people, surprisingly, were very self-sufficient economically as well as psychologically. They made everything count, down to the apple seeds. As agriculturists they had learned to utilize every drop of moisture. A delightful water boy on a donkey brought up water to each house in the village, plying his trade all day long. This saved the women from going down the trail for water. The group organization was extraordinary. All did their part, and the tasks were assigned by the village governor. It was close knit and effective.

The houses were largely built of rock, not of adobe bricks. The inner walls were plastered and whitewashed. The corn was ground by hand, and blue corn, yellow corn, and white corn were kept separate. The women made pottery, tanned the deerskins, and made the moccasins with white leggings that came to the knee. The men wove blankets and belts, did silverwork, and made beads with a primitive awl, using sea shells (got in trade from California) and turquoise. The resulting craftwork was sold and supplemented their income.

The houses were very clean and rather bare. All supplies were all kept out of sight. There was usually an iron bed, but the Pueblos slept on the floor. The bed served more as a matter of prestige than use. The mesa was at an elevation of between seven and eight thousand feet. It was cold in winter, and to get enough wood for fires was a problem. Just keeping alive required long hours of work all year round, but they preferred that to being dependent. Needless to say, they had character and self-respect.

One of them, Tom Poplitea, had a trading post at the foot of the mesa, where he kept a stock of canned tomatoes, soda pop, wheat flour, sugar, matches, and coffee, as well as the supplies of Indian agricultural products. He sold blankets and pottery and basketry to the summer tourists and was the only truck owner. Walking and riding horses were the usual modes of transportation.

The communal cornfields were at the bottom of the mesa. The apple and peach orchards were in the cracks and crevices of the rocks, where there was more moisture. Very little money changed hands; about all the trade was in barter. There was not much opportunity to cheat; it was said that nobody could out-trade a Hopi.

My next stop was at Leupp, where there was a small boarding-school infirmary.

From Leupp I went back by train to Gallup and to Thoreau on the Santa Fe Railway. Then I went by car up to Pueblo Bonito, the agency headquarters for the eastern Navahos. It was the same story there—a ramshackle hospital, one nurse, and one doctor. There was no X ray, and the practice of medicine or surgery was archaic, to put it mildly. Warmth, food, and cleanliness and aspirin were the main attractions. Obstetrics, and fractures, and malnutrition cases came in and were given care.

Often the patients, before they came to the hospital, had an Indian medicine man; sometimes they could pay for a "sing." The Navaho medicine man is really quite a psychiatrist. After the spiritual rites are satisfied, the Navaho is ready to try the white man's care. One of the interpreters said to me, "The Indians don't understand why the white doctors never ask about their dreams." I replied that there were white doctors who were interested in dreams but we had none of them in the Indian Service. Thus, psychosomatic cures are not so new after all. If one gets right with the spiritual forces, perhaps aspirin will work wonders. The antibiotics hidden in moulds and the cortizone in herbs, we don't know much about.

I was allowed to watch an Indian medicine man treating a case of pneumonia. He made hoops out of willow wands and had the patient crawl through them, hoping to catch the evil spirit that was bedeviling her. She was near delirium, very tired and cold without clothes or blankets. I found it hard to look on with equanimity. It was rigorous. I did not hear the outcome, but she evidently had faith in the efficacy of the sand painting and charms, an important part of the treatment. It cost a lot of money in sheep. The interpreter said he had started to study Indian medicine, but it took many years before the old man would transfer their power to their young apprentices. Willie wanted to get married and decided that he could get along better with a government salary of forty dollars a month as an interpreter. He also did some interpreting for one of the missionary churches. He could live well on sixty dollars a month.

There was a cynical saying in government circles about government service. Three things you must learn: (1) pass the buck, (2) stand from under, and (3) draw your pay. Pass the buck to the Indian; stand from under the superintendent, and draw your pay for yourself. Seniority will finally come your way if you follow these three rules successfully. These are the cynics' rules and consolations.

After these twelve weeks I was more than ready to get back to Washington.

In retrospect this first field trip to all the Navaho jurisdictions was very enlightening to me. Living conditions were primitive. All food had to be hauled in; government cars were dilapidated and worn out; and supplies were hard to come by. Communication by telephone was primitive over a two-wire system strung on fence posts, and breakdowns were frequent and of unpredictable duration. Costs for adequate administration were much higher than elsewhere. The upkeep of roads was simple but costly. In going from one agency to the next, the time consumed might be a day or longer, and there were six jurisdictions to be covered.

The problems were the same. Primitive habits prevailed among the Indians. Bigamy was not uncommon. Law and order was difficult, and alcoholism was gaining ground. There was no possible way to get birth records or death records. The schools were all boarding schools, and there were not enough of them. Communities remained in winter quarters only as long as food for the sheep lasted; they moved to the mountains as soon as the grass started in the spring. I didn't wonder why the administrative officials looked askance at a nurse trying to visit the homes. It was a man's job to drive through all weather. A driver-interpreter would be essential for any field nurse. But still I felt sure that public-health nursing would succeed if given a chance. After seeing the hospitals I realized that building these institutions up was really a primary need to better health service. My familiarity with the Sioux of South Dakota led me to believe that the Navahos would be just as susceptible to kindness and good care as the Sioux had been. Of course, the Navahos were living in more primitive surroundings, but they had adapted their standards successfully, and change at any point brought out obstacles that seemed insurmountable to them. The returned boarding-school pupils drifted perforce back into the traditional attitudes. One could understand it so easily. It must be a long process of growth.

I had usually stayed five days at each place and made daily trips to the outlying districts. None of the hospitals had an ambulance. The back seat of a Ford was not always adequate for a patient, and there were no station wagons available. Sometimes a truck could be rigged up to keep off the rain and snow, but the springs and tires were hard and painful. If I had not had overseas service and known how much the human frame can endure, it would have been even more difficult to conjure up a vision of a good field service. The fact that I personally enjoyed primitive living made this field trip quite a lot of fun. I used to enjoy the look of amazement when the service employees gave away their feelings about a traveler from the "Washington Office" who could rough it with pleasure. Their attitude was *"You* couldn't and wouldn't endure this." But they didn't want any sympathy. They prided themselves on their hardiness. I didn't offer them sympathy—just admiration tinged with envy.

My nearest approach to style was light-colored stockings. One old woman pinched my leg and said, "No stockings?" at which the others in the group burst out laughing. Nowadays they all wear the sheerest nylons they can find when they come to town. I am sure, though that they preferred the warmth of black cotton.

111

I carried two smallish suitcases and a briefcase with me. These held three dresses, three sweaters, one top coat, one hat, and undies. I could usually find soap flakes en route. I got the art of living in a suitcase down to a fine point. Small and light equipment was my aim.

The hours of work were eight o'clock to five-thirty, but I found that talking to people meant working in the evening hours as well. So I kept no track of time. I inspected the hospitals in the daytime but talked with individuals in the evenings. I developed a good memory for names and faces of employees. That came easily.

I think I must have consumed a ton of fried chicken and hot biscuits, but meals were not at regular hours, and after long rides out of doors in government Fords, I could use nourishment.

Polite conversation was not a concomitant of mealtimes; we addressed ourselves to the food. It was sissy to talk at the table. But that was nothing new to a nurse. A clean plate was a compliment to the cook. I scored on that. Most of the beef was pot roast; most of the chicken was fried; most of the mutton was stew, and that was it. Vegetables were canned; desserts were pie, some better than others. I did develop one dislike—canned yellow string beans. I still can't bear them.

Writing my reports to the Commissioner was a bugbear until I learned a formula:

1. Time of arrival and departure.
2. Purpose of visit.
3. Facts observed.
4. Opinions formulated—impressions of personnel.
5. Recommendations.
6. Thanks for courtesy at the jurisdiction.

112

Sometimes it was difficult to keep facts and opinions separate, but with practice it became easier. At least it gave me a plan to follow so that there was some order and similarity of approach to the problems.

XXI

Second Field Trip—The Northern Agencies

WHEN I RETURNED TO WASHINGTON IN APRIL, I felt that
I had turned up more ground than I could hope to culti-
vate and certainly that I had a big piece of work on my
hands. I was eager to know the rest of the problems. There
were a great many more Indians scattered in small groups
from Seattle down to San Diego. There were larger groups
in Minnesota, Wisconsin, and North Dakota and many
groups in Arizona besides the Navaho near Phoenix and
Tucson. Altogether, if my foot got to itching I could find
plenty of places to go. I did not want to get imbedded in
Washington because, though there was much to do there,
I felt blocked by the anomalous position I had in the Medical Division. So in August I worked out a new itinerary
for myself, taking in Mt. Pleasant, Michigan; Tomah and
Keshena in Wisconsin; the Consolidated Chippewas at Cass
Lake, Minnesota; and the Red Lake Agency, also in Minnesota; Poplar and Fort Belknap in Montana; and Idaho
and Washington states. This was pretty straight across the
northern belt of the country.

Mt. Pleasant and Tomah were nonreservation boarding
schools. At that time there began to be a good deal of talk
about state boards of health including Indian reservations
in their activities. Dr. Chesley, state public-health director
in Minnesota, was very anxious to have supervision of pub-

114

lic-health nurses among Indians on the reservations there; the government could pay them. This was arranged later.

This trip was going to be a long haul, with many different situations because the Indians were beginning to scatter looking for work. They were losing their tribal customs but were not yet given either education or health service by the state. This was very different from the Navaho situation, not as close knit.

I left Washington in September. I found the nurse at the school infirmary at Mt. Pleasant much upset because there were no bed pans in the hospital. She didn't approve of pneumonia cases getting up without wrappers or slippers to walk to the toilet. The superintendent just said, "They always had."

Here I really ran into the red tape of "the annual estimate." All supplies were ordered one year in advance. Once the annual estimate was approved by the Washington Office it seemed an insurmountable feat to buy any item that had not been ordered by the superintendent, even though it appeared on the general list from which the annual estimate had been made. The superintendent's judgment was law. About all I could say was, "If your daughter was sick with pneumonia, would you let her up to go to the toilet without a wrapper or slippers? Would you hire a nurse to take care of her and not give her the tools to work with?" He got one bed pan and one urinal. The nurse found another job during the summer vacation.

At Tomah I found a very devoted Indian woman, a graduate nurse who had taken her training at Hampton, Virginia. She was trying hard to keep a typhoid boy in bed, and because of this case no other patients had been admitted. The boy was delirious and threatened to walk home. He had had a hemorrhage. The nurse was staying up all night to keep him in bed, and all day she sat in the room

115

with him. Meals were sent to her from the employees' club. The boy was getting only milk. When I got there the superintendent had arranged to admit a four-month old baby who had tubercular meningitis. The baby was upstairs, the boy was downstairs, and the nurse was played out. I got the superintendent to hire someone to sit with the boy, and an old man of seventy-five was hired. Although the old man did nothing but sit, the nurse did have a few quiet moments to doze off. Also, I relieved her while she went over to the dining room for meals as long as I stayed there. Fortunately, perhaps, the baby died in about four days.

The next jurisdiction I went to was Cass Lake in Minnesota. The doctor there was a very hard-working man who looked after the children in the sanatorium school. But he also had got a house set up as a maternity ward and another house down the road a piece for the aged men. They had no laundry equipment and had to send the bed linens off by express to Bemidji. When the express returned in three weeks, they had clean sheets again. There was no plumbing in the house for the aged men. The food was carried over from the maternity ward in buckets, and the empty dishes were carried back to be washed. The general smell of the place was nauseous. I remember this whole visit as a nightmare.

The next place was Poplar, Montana, very much on the prairies, cold, bleak, and hard scrabble. There was a graduate nurse there who was a temporary. Her two front teeth were filled with diamonds, which gave her a flashing smile. The hospital was the usual clapboard construction. I stayed only three days, and I don't remember the doctor or the patients. I visited two day-schools to see if there was a reasonable place for a public-health field nurse but decided that other reservations offered a better chance to develop good service. The Indians were Sioux. Most of their land had been leased to white cattle ranchers. This gave the Indians some income, allowing them to live in a very poor way, but they did not have to work, and they preferred not working to the struggle necessary to improve their way of life.

The next stop was Fort Belknap and Lodgepole, Montana—two small groups of Sioux Indians about forty miles apart but under the same jurisdiction. There was a small house being used as a hospital at Fort Belknap. The cook was sleeping in the operating room because it was the warmest place in the house. There was no nurse, and the doctor was a temporary appointee. He did no surgery but could see the Indians who came in for aspirin and cod-liver oil.

I thought that the group out in the Lodgepole district would probably respond to care. They were more closely knit as a group than those living around the agency. The whole picture was the most dilapidated that I had encountered. The superintendent was trying to get the Indians started with cattle, but they were content to live on government rations and had no ambitions other than slow starvation. Of course, I didn't really know them at all, but I understood that the office had made a reservation there because the Indians had drifted in from Canada and were a sore spot that had to be reckoned with somehow. A great complaint had come to the Indian Office, and I was instructed by the Commissioner to study the situation and make recommendations concerning the rations. I believe I got oatmeal instead of rice on the ration list; they would not eat rice and would eat oatmeal. I was neither a dietitian nor a social worker, but something had to be done.

At Fort Belknap, I came to a really low moment in my attitude toward the job I had undertaken. With such poor hospital care available it seemed futile to try to establish a public-health nursing service. Since hospital personnel

117

were needed so badly my job resolved itself into a purely recruiting service for hospital nurses. I remember one Sunday at Fort Belknap sitting beside a wood stove that required stoking every ten minutes, writing to Miss Mennegerode of the Public Health Service a letter that must have been as blue as indigo. What I didn't know was that the chief of the Medical Division, Dr. Newberne, had died and that the United States Public Health Service was loaning five medical officers to reorganize the Medical Division. Miss Minnegerode showed my letter to Dr. Guthrie, the new Medical Division chief. He decided he wanted to take me into his plans, therefore I was instructed to report to Washington after completing my itinerary.

The last two assignments were in the state of Washington, Colville and Yakima, so I left Fort Belknap quite happily. For some reason I had developed the idea that once I got to Spokane the proverbial coastal climate would make everything beautiful. I dreamed all night on the train of lush roses and other floral beauty like that in southern California. And was I disappointed when I woke up in Spokane to a cold and barren country not very different from Montana!

The Colville Indians reminded me of the Sioux. They wore ten-gallon hats decorated with turkey feather plumes. They were on horseback.

The reservation had a small hospital, but it was closed because they had had no doctor for over two years. As far as any nursing service was concerned, it was a blank wall. It occurred to me that perhaps the State Board of Health would take on Indians in addition to the county nursing care. So I stayed over in Seattle on my way to Yakima to explore that opportunity. There was a course in public-health nursing in Washington University, and I contacted Mrs. Soule, the director of the course, as a possible recruiting agency for the West Coast. She was not very well estab-

118

lished, but she was enthusiastic and very willing to help me. The State Public Health Service was not interested in adding Indians to its problems. They were more inclined to let the government tend to them.

From Seattle I went down to Yakima, where the Indians were living in scattered groups. There was a field matron there who really was more of a social worker than a health worker. There was a small hospital, but I don't remember anything about it. Most of the Indians had jobs or got money from leasing their land. They were poor and not very strong in their tribal affiliations. It was an entirely different picture than the Sioux, Navaho, or Pueblo groups. They were individuals mingling freely with the culture of the white settlers.

My own state of mind was such that I had lost much of my initiative and could not even imagine trying to set up any new service there. I realized the need for better service, but with the superintendent uninterested and with only a few contract doctors, it seemed a very difficult situation. So I left, thinking it was better to leave the field matron functioning as a social worker. This was certainly a low point in my career as an organizer of nursing services.

XXII

Medical Reorganization

I WENT BACK TO WASHINGTON IN NOVEMBER to an entirely new setup of the Health Division of the Washington office. I was taken into the plans and given a desk in the Medical Division office. Dr. Marshall Guthrie was the new director on loan from the Public Health Service. He was a delightful change from poor old sick Dr. Newberne. His assistant was Dr. L. L. White, an Indian Service doctor brought in from the field. He was a cut above most of the field doctors, knew the Indians well, and also knew many of the field doctors. Dr. White did most of the correspondence and also looked after the allotments of medical funds. He knew the conditions in the service and was a good guide in helping Dr. Guthrie get acquainted with the problem. The outstanding quality of Dr. Guthrie was his patience and quiet realization that he must have more money to get much accomplished. He began by getting the salaries of the medical personnel raised to $2,400 for doctors and $1,800 for nurses. He got a policy of promotions within the grade for the then existing doctors and nurses. That was a great step forward from an initial start of $1,200 for doctors and $800 for nurses. Then came a policy of allowing vacations with pay. More positions for both doctors and nurses were allowed.

My job changed quite considerably. Instead of working

on the edge of the Health Division. I was an integral part of the setup, and responsibility for securing all nursing personnel became my immediate task. So I went into the job of recruiting nurses in all ways I could devise. I talked at state nurses' meetings and published articles both in the *American Journal of Nurses* and the *Public Health Nursing Journal.* Also I talked to the senior classes in various training schools. I wrote to any nurse who made inquiry about work in the Indian Service and became more or less expert on the typewriter. All this kept me occupied in Washington for about six months. Finally I had a secretary assigned to me, who relieved me of the time-consuming task of writing all my letters myself. I could teach her the steps in making an appointment and checking the nurse's credentials for Civil Service appointment. All this took time, but as the development of the Medical Division was a major concern of the Secretary of the Interior, we had much more favorable attention all up and down the line. There was some thrill in working with an expanding service. What a difference it made!

In 1928 the volume of work in the field and the Washington office had increased so much that I couldn't cover all the demands. The district medical directors wanted help on nursing problems in the field, and the routine correspondence about nursing was too heavy for the medical division to handle without my help. I needed an assistant who could be in Washington or in the field. Miss Minnegerode suggested one of her nurses, Miss Sallie Jeffries, whom I had known quite well at Base Hospital 5 in France during the first World War. Her home was in Virginia, and she was glad to be in Washington. I was happy over this suggestion also because she could be transferred into the Indian Service from Public Health Service, thus avoiding the Civil Service rigmarole that would have occurred if a

121

nongovernment nurse had been named. So she came. Of course she had to get some idea of conditions of work in the Indian Service and spent about four months in the field. After that she came into the Washington office to handle that job while I went out for a field trip. It was a great relief of pressure to me. We worked happily together, and I could not have asked for better help. She was wonderful in her judgment and skill with people both in the field and in the Washington office.

District territories were set up with public-health divisional medical directors at four localities, one at Albuquerque, one in Minneapolis, one in Oklahoma City, and one in Seattle. These men visited the various jurisdictions making recommendations and reports on personnel. It was a long slow uphill process, but it gave the medical men a feeling of integration and a professional future. They were no longer pawns in the keeping of the superintendent of each agency.

The next trip I made out in the field I determined that I would go to the warm climate in the hot weather and the cold climate in the winter so that I could experience personally what the nurses had to face in the way of climate. So I went to Phoenix when the thermometer was 117 degrees in the shade.

In the Southwest I ran into a new handicap in hiring personnel. There it was quite easy to hire competent nurses, but they had no job security unless they were appointed by the Civil Service.

XXIII

The Southern Trip

THERE WERE MANY SCHOOLS AND RESERVATIONS to visit in and around Phoenix; also there were a lot of good doctors. I stayed at the boarding school right in Phoenix at first. It was a big nonreservation boarding school with about four hundred children, mostly from the nearby reservations—Pima, Sacaton, Apache, Salt River, Papago, San Carlos Apaches, and quite a few Navahos. The school superintendent was Mr. John Brown, who had been in the service many years. He was a good administrator but didn't see the need for more than one nurse for his forty-bed hospital. The doctor, Fred Loe, was an old hand, too, and was skeptical of having Civil Service nursing care. The hospital was an old ramshackle wooden structure—not too hard to heat in that climate, but hard to keep clean, and inconvenient. Dr. Loe liked to do surgery and could get competent medical and nursing assistance from the town, so they had taken on more surgery than any other place I had visited. Two good practical nurses and one temporary graduate nurse were on hand. They did some obstetrics and infant care, and I thought they were doing well with what they had. About three miles east of the school was the sanatorium school of which Dr. Arthur Wheeler was in charge. This was also a large wooden structure with about six small rooms and two large wards and tent cottages.

123

They took in adults as well as children. There were two nurses, neither of them Civil Service appointees. It was not hard to hire competent nurses in the town of Phoenix, so I persuaded them to send in their papers to me at the office so that I could try to make their appointments permanent. I remember when I talked with Dr. Wheeler about sending out a permanent Civil Service appointee, he asked, "Will she be a rabbit or a wild cat?" That was a bit of a nudge on my ability to pick a nurse from paper qualifications.

Mr. Brown also had charge of the Apache and Mohave Indians living near Salt River not far from Scottsdale. I tried to sell him the idea of establishing a public-health nurse there, but he was dubious. His attitude was, "Here's another headache."

The Civil Service policy was that any nurse hired locally had no permanent status and could be replaced any time a Civil Service qualified nurse could be found to take the job. Of course, the Civil Service nurses had to serve a probationary time of six months before they achieved a permanent status. I found that the superintendent felt much happier to have the nurses that they could hire and fire if unsatisfactory; the job of justifying an unfavorable report to the Washington office and the Civil Service Commission was a headache. Superintendents often reported favorably on a nurse's probationary six months of service rather than go through the effort of making their opinion of her stick.

At Sacaton, the agency headquarters for the Pima Reservation in Arizona, Mr. Chester Faris was superintendent. He showed me around and then said he had to visit a group of Indians working for the railroad, and as there were complaints of the Indians' having trachoma, would I be willing to go with him and Dr. Mansfield to visit them? Of course, I said I would. We started out in the Doctor's car —a fearful old rattletrap with the stuffing of the back seat

124

all bursting out. We were going along the winding sandy roads of the reservation, when I smelled smoke and saw a puff of smoke coming out of the upholstery. The two men were on the front seat, and I leaned over and said, "This car is on fire."

The Doctor said in the most patronizing tone, "Oh, no, I think not," almost as if he had said, "You foolish woman from Washington, you just don't understand the rugged West."

As neither of the men was smoking, I waited a moment and said, "There is smoke coming out of the upholstery."

At that Dr. Mansfield drew to a stop, got out, and got down in the sand on his hands and knees, peering under the running board. He yelled, "My God, it *is* on fire," and began to throw handfuls of sand. Mr. Faris ripped up the front seat, and there straddled on the exhaust pipe was a government pamphlet burning merrily away. Of course, I was out of the car too. Dr. Mansfield's last handful of sand knocked the burning paper to the ground.

In another few minutes it would have ignited the oily gas tank, and we would have had it. Dr. Mansfield's respect for the supervisor from Washington increased visibly. We got back in and rattled on to Safford.

The Doctor examined the eyes, and I sat quietly by.

Dr. Mansfield said to Dr. Faris, "I don't believe it is trachoma. I think it is too much sand and glare. If they would wear dark glasses I think the tendency to the weeping and redness would clear up. Can we tell the railroad boss that we want to try this treatment and that we will get our eye specialist to see them?"

The Indians were good workmen, and the railroad wanted them. Of course the Indians felt that dark glasses made them conspicuous and endangered their jobs. They were hesitant. Then I horned in and said to their wives. "You

125

see, the glasses would help them not to rub their eyes, and if the tears stopped, people wouldn't be afraid that they had trachoma. Why don't you remind them to wear the glasses? And also if they had clean ironed handkerchiefs, people would see that they were being careful of their own eyes and knew how not to spread any eye sickness."

The women nodded in affirmation.

On the way home Mr. Faris asked me where I learned to handle Indians. I told him that I had learned on the Rosebud.

He said, "You certainly impressed these women. You were so quiet. The Pima Indians just can't bear loud talking. Sitting there quietly for ten minutes is just what is the right way to do."

So the supervisor proved not so ignorant of Indians and government Fords after all.

This was before the days of air conditioning, and it was hot. I found one ingenious nurse had constructed a homemade air conditioner with a fan, a box of wet excelsior, and a gunnysack fitted into her bedroom window frame. It did bring down the temperature almost 10 degrees. That made it possible to sleep better. Whoever said that nurses won't take hardships just didn't know nurses. I may say that when I got off the train at Needles at 123 degrees I decided that the field matron there was going to be hard to replace with a field nurse. The Indians were of the Colorado River tribe. People who worked with them liked them, but I did not feel drawn toward them. Tremendously fat and slow moving in both mind and body, they lived in one or two-room square wooden houses. The men mostly worked for the railroad. The field matron was doing social work and trying to inculcate sanitation. It was a very slow changeover. I had been to the Colorado River Indian Reservation at

126

Parker just before getting off at Needles so had seen the reservation background of this tribe.

On the reservation they lived in wickiups which were made of willow wands, tied together at the top with a smoke hole near the center. The wickiups were small, crowded, and smoky in the winter and were only used for storage in the summer, when the people lived out of doors under a square structure covered over with branches. The cooking and washing were all done outdoors. They lay about in the shade in the heat of the day, which was all day in the summer. The problem of storage was something. There were no screened cupboards, and flies and dogs abounded. The Papagos and the Pimas lived in much the same fashion, but they were physically more energetic than the Colorado River group. I stayed forty-eight hours in Needles, and that was long enough to see the problem, get acquainted with the field matron, and decide that one-half of ones energy went off in sweat!

I then proceeded to Riverside, California, which was a big nonreservation boarding school and also the headquarters for the Mission Agency, which supervised a collection of the groups of Indians scattered through the mountains back of San Diego. This was the "Ramona" country, where the Indians had encountered Spanish civilization in the early days of the missions. The Indians had land up in the hill country; they worked for ranchers. They had very little medical care and could profit by a public-health nurse very evidently. We established a nurse at Banning who was to cover quite a wide territory from Palm Springs down to San Jacinto. It worked out very well. She could arrange hospital care in several localities and with various contract doctors.

From there I went up to Bishop, part of the Death Valley

desert country. At Bishop the Indians were Paiutes and Digger Indians, and there were not as many white ranchers here. There was a small hospital in one of the agency buildings, but a hospital nurse was needed. They had a contract doctor, so the nurse would have to carry a good many responsibilities—I knew the kind of nurse I would have to find.

From there in November I went to Ukiah, which has faded from my memory, and on to Hoopa Valley. I still remember the trip into Hoopa Valley. It had rained and snowed, and the agency car, driven by the superintendent, got stuck at Willow Creek. What a road! Mud about ten inches deep and sticky mud at that—gumbo. I knew it from Rosebud days. I pulled out some galoshes and helped by pushing. Finally the wheels established some traction, and the car pulled out, me running after it. As the superintendent did not come to a stop, I jumped on the running board and climbed over the car door—wet to the knees, breathless, but triumphant.

XXIV

The Northern Trip

I LEFT WASHINGTON the twenty-second of September. The temperature stood at 102 degrees. By the time I got to Minneapolis the snow was deep, and by the time I got to Bemidji the temperature was about 10 degrees below zero. We were to make the twenty-mile drive to Red Lake with four horses on a big sled. The sled had a tent nailed on it, and a stove inside the tent was to keep us warm. We struggled through snow with the sled rocking sideways and jerking forward. It took us four hours to make the twenty miles. It was hot and then cold, and I got more and more queasy. Never was I gladder to feel firm ground under my galoshes. I ran up the pathway to the employees' building where I was to spend the night. I had great respect for the nurses who learned to live with the North. I suppose if the contrast with Washington had been more gradual I could have adapted more easily. I had come to find out what cold weather was like for the field nurses, and I found out quite enough.

From Red Lake I went on to North Dakota. This time I was traveling by car. The roads were cleared, and I was making the trip with Mr. Roy Nash, who was a friend of my brother in Brazil. Mr. Nash was a gay bachelor, very palpably a lady's man. Since we were near the Canadian line, he suggested that we cross over into Canada and get some real beer and some supper. So we turned north, stopped at the border U.S. Immigration office, and then drove gaily on. We came to a crossroad and found our way blocked by police cars. We drew up with some six Canadian Mounted Police looking on and were advised that we had not checked in at the Canadian Immigration office. It didn't help much for us to say that we hadn't noticed it! Then they asked why we were in Canada. When we explained, we were told to find the office in the town where we were planning to have our glass of beer and see what the office there would tell us to do. Of course, all this took time, and when we got to the hotel it was eight o'clock. The bar was closed, and all that we could get was some of the worst 2 per cent beer I've ever tasted. When we finally got to Fort Berthold the story got there ahead of us, and a pleasant time was had by all and sundry. Of course Mr. Nash had said to me on the way out from Canada, "By George, I think they thought I was bringing you in for immoral purposes."

So it was all very funny; I couldn't tell whether my stock went up or down as a supervisor of nurses! I took the ribbing with a grin. It quieted down and wasn't relayed to Washington, until I told it on myself, on my return.

XXV

A Big Change

WHEN HERBERT HOOVER BECAME PRESIDENT IN 1929 and
Ray Lyman Wilbur became secretary of the interior there
was scarcely a ripple felt in the rank and file of office employees. Another Republican. But when Commissioner
Burke resigned for reasons of health and two Democrats
were appointed, we began to wonder what had happened.
Mr. Charles J. Rhoads and Mr. Henry Scattergood were
both Quakers from Philadelphia. They had been active in
the Friends Service Committee, and that explained Mr.
Hoover's choice. Mr. E. B. Merritt, a Democrat, who had
been assistant commissioner for twenty years, was transferred to the legal department of the Department of the
Interior. This gave a really new slant to the Bureau of
Indian Affairs. So many years of tight control on finances
made us all fearful that political mincemeat would be made
of the two innocent Friends in Congressional committees,
but they stood up very favorably.

There was no fanfare of change. It was quiet and orderly.

Mr. Rhoads and Mr. Scattergood divided their fields of
interest, Mr. Scattergood concentrating on economic and
property interests and Mr. Rhoads on personnel, education
and health services. We did hear by the grapevine that
there would be a new policy of securing more trained personnel, especially personnel trained in social work.

131

The two new social workers were Mr. Robert Lansdale and Miss Mary McGair. They were not appointed to existing jobs but were rather supernumeraries whose function was not too clearly stated but was advisory to the new commissioner and his assistant. They were supposed to review correspondence, study the problems, and make suggestions to the various heads of divisions. All this was hard for the old-line officials to gauge and adjust to. The old officials had grown up with the service and knew the laws and policies and political strengths of various personnel. The newcomers did not meddle much with either the Education Division or the Medical Division, but with Law and Order and Property Administration they studied and reviewed policies and programs. Naturally they were resented to an uncertain extent, but they were reasonable and not inflexible. I liked both of them and enjoyed talking with them. They certainly had a lot to learn about both bureaucracy and administration as found in the Indian Service of those days.

With one group all for maintaining the status quo and a new group bent on changes, there was a good deal of confusion of the old established lines of thought. For instance, there were over eleven thousand laws applicable to the Indians of Oklahoma which did not apply to the Indians of other states. These laws were not codified and were often contradictory. It was a tangle—hard to understand and even more difficult to reduce to terms of program and procedure.

Education under Mr. Peairs had been pretty well stabilized, but a new supervisor in Primary Education was appointed to deal primarily with day schools. For secondary schools Mr. Peairs now had an assistant. Mr. Peairs had long been in charge also of Haskell Institute and had built a very creditable institution patterned on Hampton Insti-

132

tute. Haskell included grades four through ten. When Mr. Peairs later retired, the Education Division was headed by W. Carson Ryan, whose headquarters were in Washington. I don't know much about the chronology of the changes in the Education Division, but there were a good many, including the use of public schools whenever possible.

In the Health Division the biggest change was a gradual change in financial status. Better salaries attracted more doctors. Also, beyond filling the then existing positions for doctors, there was a need for more positions. Improvements in these matters came about gradually, and during the Hoover administration we began to feel we were "cooking with gas."

The help of the United States Public Health Service was invaluable in changing the existing conditions in the Medical Division. Dr. Guthrie knew well the technique of advising and supervising service. He was quiet and firm and put his finger on the sorest spots. His work with the Congressional committee was dexterous and successful. He got more money for salaries for the doctors and nurses as well as more flexible policies for vacations with pay. When I came to realize the interrelations of policies, program, procedure, and personnel on an advisory rather than a mandatory basis, I began to see its usefulness.

I remember one technique taught me by Dr. Guthrie— the way to deal with an unco-operative superintendent was just to draw a circle around him, isolate him. It took about two years to bring him around, but he came! Smarting but out smarted.

Transfer of location of field personnel was allowed quite freely but had to be justified to the Department of the Interior. It was the most intricate kind of jigsaw puzzle I had ever tried to piece together. The objective of improved service and *esprit de corps* was a tall tree to climb in a

133

hurry. Our critics couldn't wait for slow growth. To get better personnel and give them a real opportunity to function was quite a task.

There was another Indian Office technique that had been used for years between the office and the field. This was the circular letter from the commissioner of Indian affairs to the field service. It was supposed to carry an almost mandatory influence in the field. It was prepared by the Division, signed by the commissioner, and sent out in mimeograph form to all superintendents of reservations and schools. It might contain changes of policy, new programs, or new procedures and was supposed to be a quite sacred liaison between the Washington office and the field. Used too often, it had come to be regarded in the field with more ridicule than sanctity, but it did serve as a source of information. At Fort Hall in Idaho I found a bound looseleaf folder of all the circulars they had received, containing, among other things, a recipe for "Government Whitewash" that seemed to me quite sardonic. It wasn't meant to be anything more than informational but could be twisted into a wickedly distorted inference.

I got hold of good nursing personnel, and it really began to be fun to see improvement all along the line. There were plenty of obstructions to overcome, but with the help of good nursing personnel the policies became more evident and the procedures more orderly. By and large the nurses were happy. Of course, we got hold of one or two crackpots, but on the whole the nurses liked the Indians and the Indians liked the nurses. Matrimony cut into the ranks occasionally but not as often as one might expect. I did not try to develop a "corps"; white uniforms in the hospital, blue uniforms in the field, and white caps in the hospital, with black velvet strips for the head nurses, were customary but not regulation. I frowned on smoking on duty, but there

was not much occasion to lay down the law on professional conduct. The nurses had learned what constituted
good professional conduct in their training-school days.
When rings and bracelets appeared, I may have said a word
or two on cleanliness, but I don't recall any great struggles
on the subject. We were simple, busy, and happy to be filling the needs.

The social life was a little barren but not very different
from back home. Making a successful adjustment to the
Indians required some dexterity, but the nurses enjoyed it.
Today we would call this a *challenge,* but then it was just
good common sense, good humor, and flexibility.

Nursing techniques varied but were uniform enough so
that I did not have to worry much about procedures. I do
remember one occasion when I found a nurse giving a
douche to a woman standing in the shower bath, and I
expostulated to her about the effectiveness of the treatment.
She admitted that she had not been taught to do it that way,
so I mentioned the incident to the head nurse and told her
to watch for such slips and see that such shortcuts were
not habitual.

On the whole the nurses were well educated in nursing
and did not require that kind of supervision from me. They
enjoyed the variety of their work and the responsibility
that they carried. They worked hard and well. Of course,
some of them missed the bright lights and new movies, but
they solaced themselves with radios, books, knitting, and
embroidery. There were a few troublemakers but not many,
and they usually sought more fertile fields after six months
of isolation. Their quarters were adequate but not fancy.
Beau parlors were not supplied, but they had heat and
light and comfortable beds and chairs. A common room,
perhaps with a piano and a kitchenette and refrigerator, was
really what they wanted. These comforts were not avail-

able at first but began to be constructed as Congress allowed the funds and the number of nurses increased.

My own life was rosy with work, progress, and interest. In 1926 I bought a little shack in Georgetown on the wrong side of the tracks. It was tumbling down, but with a mortgage I remodeled it and made it more livable. It was my first venture into the realm of property and paid off very pleasurably. I had a garden and a kitchen, and what more could I ask for after ten hours at a desk! When I went on field trips I could rent it or lock it up. I bought a car and was more than contented with life. The stock-market crash in 1929 did not bother me; I skimmed through that without loss. I never had been interested in making money and had not begun to save much out of my $2,600 a year. I had enough to live simply and no responsibilities other than myself. I was so well and strong that the future of old age had not seemed to be looming very near. I saved a little but not enough to whet my appetite for more. The years rolled on without disaster of any kind interfering with my personal plan of life.

After we acquired two nurses for each hospital, it became evident that the only fair division of work was to take turns doing the night shift. This worked reasonably well, but as the work increased and more nurses were added to the staff, the need for having one nurse with more managerial duties and the others appointed to staff duties led to setting up a head-nurse position at an advanced salary. Seniority was an easy and acceptable ruling but not always successful. The qualities required for head nurses are quite different than those of good staff nurses. There are a few nurses who prefer bedside nursing to managing other workers. The head nurse had to arrange and supervise the duties for all the hospital employees, nurses, attendants, ward maids, cooks, janitors, orderlies, clerks, and technicians.

136

This meant that she had to work closely with the doctor in charge. Personality played a great part in her ability to function. The required attributes are hard to select from paper. Experience in that sort of work is some help and shows on the paper records, but the real test is on the job.

This made it all the more necessary to observe the nurses on the job. Some doctors did not want to be relieved of all this petty detail, and some nurses couldn't carry the load without friction, but we finally did get the tangles smoothed out, and new staff nurses were more easily inducted into the service because the conditions of work were comparable to conditions in civilian hospitals. I became a past master at straightening out tangles and misunderstandings, making each person feel valuable and valued. It sometimes took a lot of patient listening to petty complaints and hurt feelings but was rewarding, on the whole.

We did not appoint married nurses in those years because there were usually not quarters available for their husbands. Neither did we appoint Negro nurses—not because we were prejudiced but because to add a third racial group to be dealt with in an isolated situation with plenty of prejudice among doctors, nurses, and Indians seemed to me somewhat unkind to the nurse who had to pay her way to the station. She was licked before she started. Several years later we did try it out in Oklahoma and California, but one of the Negro nurses was unable to adjust to the demands of the job, and the other was unhappy in the isolation and resigned after eight months, though she said that everyone had been kind to her.

In the field I had no administrative authority, only some administrative weight. Just how much administrative weight I had was an unknown quantity. When I first was appointed by Commissioner Burke, I was looked upon as his fair-haired girl, but that I did not make any effort to cash in on his interest in the nursing work surprised the old line of Bureau employees. They became interested in training me in the accepted technique of office procedure. And I became very interested in implementing my own ideas of how to recruit nurses.

In those days there was no Federal Administrative Authority. The field superintendents supposedly had to carry out the purpose of the Congress. The commissioner had a flock of some ninety superintendents to watch over. All the supervisory personnel, including myself, reported to the commissioner on their findings and recommendations, sending a carbon copy to the agency superintendent. The superintendent could comment on my findings and recommendations if he chose, and he usually did, but there was no black-handed criticism. Of course, when in Washington my opinion of various superintendents was occasionally called for, but the general opinion about each superintendent was pretty well founded on correspondence. Like the rest of the human race, superintendents had their long and short suits.

At that time there was real decentralization in the federal administration. The local superintendent might have to justify his expenditures to the Comptroller General's office in Washington, but even that hurdle could be circumvented by an act of Congress.

I went on with the purpose of my visit to the agencies— to get acquainted and understand the existing conditions that nurses would have to meet.

The New Deal swept into office with plenty of fanfare. I went down to the Capitol to see the beginning of the Roosevelt inaugural parade. The first Democrat since Woodrow Wilson was bound to be exciting. His physical handicap was compensated by much élan, and everyone was full of the excitement of victory.

We expected many changes not only in the top echelons but quite far down in the bureaucratic personnel. Mr. Rhoads and Mr. Scattergood, being good Democrats, didn't know whether they would be retained or removed.

Mr. Ickes was suggested as the new commissioner of Indian affairs, but when he came to see Mr. Roosevelt, he was chosen as the secretary of the interior.

After Mr. Ickes was appointed, the rumors were that Mrs. Ickes had a paramount interest in Indian affairs, gained by a visit to a trading post on the Navaho Reservation near Gallup, New Mexico. So we were all keen to find out something about Mrs. Ickes. We knew she had been very much interested in Hull House in Chicago, had divorced her first husband in favor of Mr. Ickes, who had been her furnace boy in Palo Alto, and that she was rich and of a good family, but all this was not very reassuring to the men in the office; however, it did not trouble me. I had been brought up on the glories of Hull House and though not a feminist could easily see that a woman's judgment might prove of value.

We heard that there was mounting Congressional pressure for Mr. E. B. Merritt to be made commissioner of Indian affairs.

I had my first interview with Mr. Ickes when he was deciding how to avoid appointing Mr. Merritt.

Mr. E. B. Merritt, formerly assistant commissioner for twenty years, wanted the job and was the choice of Senator Joe Robinson, of Arkansas. Mr. Ickes wanted information about Mr. Merritt's technique in building up a strong following among Indian Service personnel. I was called up to the Secretary's office and was being interviewed by his legal adviser when Mr. Ickes came in. He wondered if Mr. Merritt had promised me promotion and advancement. As he had not done so, I wouldn't say that he had. Mr. Ickes was sure that he had and finally said to me, "Don't be afraid. I will protect you." I rejoined, "Protect me from what, Mr. Ickes?" He must have thought I was a simpleton, for he flung himself out of the room. I thought Mr. Ickes's offer of protection was in the same general category of what he was trying to pin on Mr. Merritt. The interview was over, and I went back to my desk.

Then came the rumor that Mrs. Ickes was going to be influential in the selection of a New Deal for the Indian Service.

When we heard that she had fallen under the spell of John Collier, who was then stirring the pot in California and was one of the most persistent and vituperative critics of the Indian Service, we became more wary. After six months of waiting for Mr. Ickes to make up his mind what to do about appointing a new commissioner and a new assistant commissioner, the blow fell. It was to be Mr. John Collier, whom we knew, and Mr. Zimmerman, whom we didn't know. Neither of these men had had experience with government organization, but neither of them wished to be a bureaucrat.

In a few days a message from the Secretary's office was passed down inviting us to contribute twenty-five cents apiece for a floral offering for Mr. Collier, and our presence was requested in the front office to watch Mr. Collier be given the oath of office. We all trooped up as bidden. Mr. Ickes opened his remarks by saying that Mr. Collier was chosen because of his long-time knowledge of the Indian problem. Then he went on to say that the Indian Office was a veritable Augean Stable and that he hoped Mr. Collier would clean it out. He didn't indicate where the manure would be used. Then we went politely forward, were introduced individually, and retired to our desks. Our bouquet disappeared, and we carried on with our desk work, sorry to say good-bye to Mr. Rhoads and Mr. Scattergood, who had worked manfully with "the Augean Stable" for four and a half years.

We knew that if our jobs were abolished we would be out, so a ripple of jitters could be felt. But that could not last long when there were five mails a day to be answered. As an introduction it was not calculated to consolidate much *esprit de corps*. We all wondered whose head would come off first. True to their training and experience, the heads of divisions tried to carry out their work to suit the new boss. But where his ideas crossed the ideas of Congress, Mr. Collier could only be so advised.

The first major change of procedure came about when the Secretary of Interior ruled that all appointments be made by him instead of the Commissioner. This boiled down to an enlarged personnel division in the Secretary's office. The net result was that in order to get a nurse on the job my recommendation had to go over seventeen desks instead of four. This slowed the appointment routine tremendously. From a possible three-day wait it was usually three or four months before a nurse got her instructions to report for duty. By that time most of the applicants had taken other jobs. The Washington payroll was heavily increased. Speed went down the drain.

One incident occurred in the appointment field of my endeavor. I read in the newspaper that Mr. Ickes had had a quarrel with a politico of Wisconsin, named Hanson. Within two months I selected a nurse from the Civil Service list, named Hanson, from Wisconsin. She was interested in the job, and I wrote her under the Commissioner's direction that I had recommended her for appointment. I sent the papers of recommendation up to the Secretary's office. Weeks went by, and then I received a letter from her asking when she might expect instructions to proceed

141

on duty. I answered her that I could not even hazard a guess. She waited for about three months, then took another job. It took the Secretary's office six months to find out that she was not a relative of the Mr. Hanson with whom Mr. Ickes had tangled. When her appointment came through, she refused with some asperity. Bureaucratic pettifogging, I had the satisfaction of naming it to myself.

After Mr. Collier was installed, we were advised by the Secretary's office that certain words must never be applied to Indians. One of them was the word "lazy." We should not even think of it. We were adjured that their work rhythm was not like ours. We were no longer to think they were indolent or lazy.

In 1934 the Wheeler-Howard Reorganization Act was passed. This was to implement Mr. Collier's ideas of the New Deal for Indians. I did not study it or formulate any opinions about it, though I knew it would bring about many changes as it filtered down to active procedures. Whether or not it would be effective against the encroachments of white economic interests would remain to be seen.

In a few months we began to hear of the anthropological approach as the new solution to the conduct of the Indian Service. An anthropologist was employed for field studies and later a tour of duty in the Washington office. I recall only one recommendation that she made to the Medical Division. She told us that the Papago Indians were very averse to having anything that was associated with their bodies burned, therefore she recommended that all the dressings, etc., be buried, not burned. The ground around their reservation was sandy, and trenches could be dug. I had visions of dirty dressings being exhumed by dogs and left around the landscape to be sunned and aired. I remember Dr. Guthrie's saying, "Oh, pshaw," and the recommendation went to files. However, these ideas had other

142

repercussions. The field service was puzzled but willing to make an effort to comply. The anthropological approach *did* have repercussions on the nursing service.

One such repercussion occurred when a head nurse, after a major amputation on an Indian, sent the leg over to the central furnace to be burned. The engineer, part Indian, refused and sent it back to the hospital, where it lay on the front porch. The head nurse called the Superintendent, who ordered that it be buried. So the head nurse asked for a man to dig, but the soil was hard. Nevertheless, the leg was covered with dirt, but not so deep but that the Superintendent's favorite German shepherd dog smelled it out and disinterred it and carried it over to the Superintendent's porch. While this problem presented the much-talked-of criticism of our lack of the anthropological approach, the Superintendent ordered that the leg be burned, and it was burned. The head nurse was not dissolved in tears. We had a good laugh.

On another field trip I found the nurse in tears. The group of Indians with whom she was working believed that every baby born in the hospital got his soul from some recently dead or dying patient. The maternity rooms were on the second floor, and she was the only nurse on duty. After tending the obstetric case she came downstairs to find all the beds empty. All the patients had decamped to save their souls, and she was sure she would be fired for neglect of duty. I happened in just in time to save her!

Mr. Collier was determined that the Washington office needed more education in the anthropological approach.

In this effort to improve the ideas of the administration in Washington the Indian Office made a grand effort and sent about twenty-five of the Indian Office personnel to the annual meeting of the anthropological association which took place in Pittsburgh. The junket cost about five thousand dollars and was considered very important because there was a speech on the Navaho scheduled. We went to Pittsburgh and sat through appalling speeches by the leading lights in the anthropological profession.

However, I enjoyed the remarks of Miss Margaret Mead. Miss Mead had been in Samoa and was much interested in the cultural mores of the Polynesians. Evidently cultural mores were not then generally considered a part of anthropology. This was a new idea being brought into the field of anthropological study. I gathered from the meeting that there were two schools of thought among anthropologists. Frank Boaz of Columbia was a leading light in the cultural studies. Ales Hrdlicka was the old type of student mainly interested in the study of skeletal differences found in man. Mr. Hrdlicka was known affectionately as Hard Liquor.

Finally, the fourth day, came the Navaho speech. We were all there.

A spidery little professor was on the platform with a blackboard filled with figures. He rose and with a pointer gave a dissertation on the skeletal structure of the Navaho. He proved to his own satisfaction that the Navaho skeletons showed that they had a "fifth caudal condyle that was spurious," that is to say, the Navaho had an extra tail bone. I think that he had no recommendations for the Indian Service personnel, and many of us felt that the work piling up on the desks in Washington would require a lot of night work to catch up.

The number of government employees had increased so much by 1934 that the Indian Office was moved out of the Interior building to one of the old army structures down in the Mall. The walls were thin, the heat was excessive, and the offices were far from soundproof. Each division had to find money to help pay a new employee who was to draw up a master plan for the field service. In our division his room was next to the medical office, and for six months we had to turn a deaf ear to his droning dictation. The net result of his master plan for the Navaho Reservation was that any letter containing the word "Navaho" had to have twelve carbon copies, as we were adjured to keep everybody informed. The stenographic load became so heavy that I got a new clerk.

Soil-erosion control became of paramount interest for the saving of Indian land, if not the Indian. It was so important that the quarters allowed by Congress to be built for field nurses on the Navaho Reservation were commandeered for soil-erosion specialists, and the field-nurse service went down the drain. It was a little disheartening to bear this sort of encroachment, but nothing could be done about it. The nurses were gone.

Another big change came about with the New Deal. Gradually the "advisory" status of Washington to the field was changed to a mandatory status. Letters were too slow, and telegrams and telephone calls were substituted. This change took time to achieve, but it was a very major administrative difference. We were being federalized.

Another big change was noticeable. We all knew that the upper echelon conducted much business during their social activities. About that time for many of the new employees cocktail parties became the accepted place to do business and enhance one's prestige. It was expensive and unpleasant, and I did not indulge in it.

During the summer of 1934, Mr. and Mrs. Ickes gave a reception for the Commissioner and the Indian Office, and we were bidden to come to the Sulgrave Club after work for drinks and refreshments. We all came to work in our best bibs and tuckers, and at four-thirty we trooped to the Sulgrave Club. There must have been some disagreement between Mr. and Mrs. Ickes as neither was present to receive us. We stood around. Mr. and Mrs. Collier were there, but no formal receiving line could be arranged with neither host nor hostess present. Finally Mrs. Ickes towered into the room. Individually we sidled up to her. Mr. Ickes appeared one-half hour later. As an introduction to the social amenities it was a flop. We retired to the obscurity of our workaday world with our tongues in our cheeks. You can't make a silk purse out of a sow's ear, and we knew where we belonged. We did not feel flattered.

There was an ephemeral social group that I saw occasionally, called "The Women in Government." We had dinner or Sunday lunch with each other now and again in small groups. Twice a year the large group was bidden by Mrs. Roosevelt to tea at the White House in winter and to a garden party in the summer. It was fun to see how it was done and was supposed, I am sure, to add to our sense of importance. I daresay it did. Mrs. Roosevelt was a simple and charming hostess.

One of the many changes made by the New Deal was a revolving fund to be spent for higher education for Indians. Many went to college, and many of the girls took nurse's training. Some of them preferred to work out of the Indian Service after graduation, but many came into the service and did very good work. I did not urge any promise of working in the Indian Service. I felt that the girls should be free to make their own choice. They had made good, and I did not want them to be subjected to any sense of inferiority.

There was no way for me to control the superiority complexes of the white personnel. The common phrase—"good, considering she's an Indian"—was devastatingly hard to overcome.

The Society of Colonial Dames sponsored six Indian girls in Philadelphia and Minneapolis hospitals during their

146

courses of study. Primarily the Dames helped look after the girls during their off-duty time and offered friendly contacts. The superintendents of nurses took special interest in their adjustment to life in a big hospital training school. Contrary to some expectations, none of the six students failed in their efforts to measure up to standards, though of course it was more difficult for some than for others. As an experiment in education, I thought it worked out well.

One of the congressmen from Oklahoma was very anxious that an Indian Service nurse's training school be started. We studied the cost and, on the basis of the army's experience at Walter Reed Hospital, persuaded him to be content with a school for attendants. We worked out a course of training at Lawton, Oklahoma, which was so successful that we carried out the same plan in several of the other large hospitals. All the graduates were in demand, the salary was $1,080, and the experience served to show the Indian girls whether they would like to take up nursing as a profession.

Early in the New Deal I had a great satisfaction in being asked to stay after office hours and help spend $3,500,000 for hospital construction. It took just forty-five minutes. I had made more recent field trips than either of the doctors, and I knew just how impossible the old structures were for nurses, doctors, and patients. Of course, we didn't think we would get much of the money, but it was fun to outline our needs to the White House. In due time funds were made available, and we benefited to quite a large extent by the money spent for new construction.

XXVI

New Deal Programs

THERE WAS A NEW PROGRAM entitled "The Preservation of Indian Art." It was thoroughly worthwhile. But the following story was enjoyed by many who knew Emmett Wirt, the trader at Dulce, New Mexico.

He was an old lumberman who had been with the Apaches for twenty years as a trader. He was not impressed by "the government" and could easily face down any official.

There was a great hue and cry over preserving the art of the Indians, and a very well-dressed lady got off the little narrow-gauge train locally called the Chili Line which ran from Alamosa to Santa Fe through Dulce and Chama. It wound through the mountains over shaky trestles and through smoky tunnels.

When the train reached Dulce, a rather elegant-looking lady picked her way through the muddy street and on arriving at Emmett Wirt's trading post announced with an air designed to impress, "Mr. Wirt, Secretary Ickes sent me to talk with you."

Mr. Wirt was busy waiting on two Indian women. He continued with the Indian women, not even acknowledging Mrs. Whoosit's remark. There was a large can over in the corner, and he directed a mouthful of tobacco juice toward the can. Mrs. Whoosit moved to one side and said again,

"Mr. Ickes sent me here to ask you what kind of art of the Apaches should be preserved."

Emmett answered, "Do you want to know what I think?"

Mrs. Whoosit brightened up, and she answered, "Of course I do. Mr. Ickes sent me here to find out what you think."

"Well," Emmett said, "you tell Mr. Ickes that I think that the government is pissing against the wind."

Mrs. Whoosit said, "Oh, Mr. Wirt! I can't tell him that."

"Well," said Emmett, "that's what I think."

The train had pulled out, and she was taken to the mission to await the train on the following day.

An early encounter with Mr. Collier, when the New Deal was pretty well established and one could expect almost any new vista on the horizon, was one of those occasions when you have to say "No" to an idea about which you have no personal feeling but know that it isn't going to work as a plan of action. You know the plan's initiation is predicated on a lack of knowledge.

Mr. Collier was a small man but full of big ideas. He liked to conjure up new ventures. He called for me to come to the front office, and when I got there I found him sitting cross-legged on his desk, chewing his necktie. The substance of his remarks was that he wanted me to issue orders to the nurses to teach the Indian women birth control. I could hardly believe my ears. Apart from the medical co-operation involved, I mentioned that the Catholic church would be up in arms pretty quickly, but that didn't trouble him. He wanted a program of birth control. So I asked him what kind of a program. Did he want the nurses to recommend the current drugstore technique? His answer was, "Yes. Why not?" My answer was, first because it was ineffective, and second that nurses would not care to undertake that type of instruction. It belonged, if anywhere, in the medical field; it was not nursing. We were proud of having helped to reduce the infant mortality rate but were not trained to tackle the birth rate. I am quite sure that he thought I had moral scruples concerning birth control, but my scruples were against poor medical practice. At that time vinegar douches were the home remedy to control conception. I knew that method was not effective, but I also knew that a first-rate birth-control clinic required much more than a zealous nurse. And I knew that neither nurses nor doctors in the service were ready for that type of program on the Indians. So with what grace I could muster, I refused to follow up any such program. I never knew whether Mr. Collier really was determined to institute this policy or whether he hoped I would walk out on a limb that he could then saw off. But I stayed well within the limits of professional ethics and let it go at that. I never heard any more of it. It did not enhance my respect for him nor my trust in his administrative wisdom.

In the course of the next five years there were more ups than downs in the medical program.

One of the interesting co-operative medical efforts was with the tuberculosis institute of Baltimore. Dr. Esmond Long wanted to try out a large experiment of immunization of new-born infants with B.C.G. vaccine. He loaned the Indian Service an expert epidemiologist, Dr. Joseph F. Aronson, to work on various Indian reservations where the incidence of tuberculosis was high. The field nurse could help find the infants and talk to the parents. Of course, the reservation doctors could also guide Dr. Aronson on case histories of adults in the families. Twenty-five years later, according to the United States Public Health Service findings in 1957, there had not been an exact study of the results of this program, owing largely to limited personnel for the proper follow-up. About all we know is that the rate of tuberculosis has decreased, although it is still five times as high as for all other races in the United States.

XXVII

Expanding Territory

ABOUT THIS TIME the affairs of Alaskan Indians and Eskimos were shifted from the Office of Education to the Office of Indian Affairs. The Office of Education had employed a few doctors and nurses, but they were under the guidance of a Ph.D., with no professional medical guidance. When they were put under the Indian Office a new Public Health Service doctor, on loan as district medical director, Dr. Van Ackren, was there the first year and then Dr. Vance Murray the second year. The third assignment was Dr. L. M. Fellows.

The Indians were down along the coast near Juneau and inland on the Tanana and Yukon rivers. The Eskimos were on the coast above Nome and on the Kuskoquim and Yukon rivers. There were seven small hospitals, each with a doctor in charge, and twelve nurses at large, visiting the widely separated villages. There were day schools and two or three boarding schools. I had been covering territory from Miami, Florida, to Neah Bay, Washington. This pushed my territory up to Point Barrow, Alaska, east and west from Dutch Harbor to Syracuse, New York. I did not give Alaska much thought, though I knew that the nurses at large made two extended trips a year, one by dogsled in the winter and one by gas boat in the summer. They had been functioning without professional supervision for years under the Office of Education, and I had plenty to do without doing more than recruit if Dr. Fellows asked for more nurses. Matters continued this way for six months before Dr. Fellows asked that I come up and visit as many nurses as I could between July and October—after the mosquito season and before the freezeup.

I was totally ignorant about Alaska. I had selected two field nurses, and they were on duty, one at Wainwright on the coast and one at Tanana Crossing about one hundred miles east of Fairbanks, for the Indians on the Tanana River. Nobody told me to take a pair of pants along, but there were no docks north of Nome. I would have to climb down the ship's side on a rope ladder into an Eskimo skin boat to land. I blush to think of the display of pink bloomers that the Eskimos saw north of Nome. If anyone *had* told me, I think I might have reneged, because if there is one thing I dislike more than a narrow plank across a stream, it is a ladder. To jump from the bottom rung of a rope ladder into a skin boat (oomiak) full of Eskimos was really an ordeal. The Eskimo language sounds like a chorus of clickety-clack. I could only tell when to jump by the rising crescendo of noise from the skin boat. But there I was, and I knew I was being judged, so I couldn't afford to be scared. If I landed in the Arctic Ocean, there were lots of people there to fish me out, but I could swim or float.

To give you a more orderly narrative, I go on to Alaska. The Department of the Interior ran a small ocean-going steamer, the *North Star*. It carried one year's supply of food, lumber, hardware, and special orders to the various government stations where doctors, nurses, and schools were situated, but mission stations had to afford commercial freight.

The *North Star* left Seattle early in August and went via the Inland Passage up to Juneau then out to Dutch Harbor,

153

where both a school and a hospital were located, then back to Seward, up the coast to Nome, then up to Point Barrow and back to Seattle, a trip of about fifteen hundred miles each way. I was on board. Going by the Inland Passage between Canadian mainland and many large and small islands off Canada, there was no rough sea, so the passage was delightfully smooth. It was more like a canal trip than an ocean voyage.

Our first stop was Ketchikan, where we stopped only to let off a new doctor and his wife. They were going to the island of Metlakatla. On the dock stood the village nurse, Mrs. Leta Pearson. I could only talk to her a few minutes. That morning she had delivered her two hundred eighty-third baby. She was busy all of her time in Ketchikan, where there were big salmon-canning plants. You could smell them a mile away. Mrs. Pearson was an ample, middle-aged soul. You could see devotion and hard work all over her face and figure. Program and procedures could not be judged so accurately at that distance.

Leaving Ketchican, we went to Wrangell, where I debarked. In Wrangell I encountered the ubiquitous wooden duck-board paths that lifted one above the wet, soggy swamp found on all the low ground. At a boarding school called Wrangell Institute there was a temporary nurse. The health program was not well organized—just a hit-or-miss affair built around the needs as the school superintendent saw them. The school nurse also visited in the villages of Wrangell and Petersburg. The doctor was on contract to the school. Both these villages were relatively well-to-do. I had left the *North Star* on Saturday and left Wrangell for Juneau early Monday morning on a commercial coastwise steamer, the *Aleutian*. There were village nurses at Saxman, Hydaburg, Klawak, and Kake whom I missed seeing. I was eager to get to Juneau and plan my time with Dr. Fellows.

154

When the *Aleutian* docked at 8 P.M. in Juneau, Dr. Fellows was there to greet me and take me to the hotel. I also met Mr. Hawkesworth, chief of the Alaska Division of Indian Affairs. I had four days in Juneau to get my itinerary and background information lined up. I inspected the hospital and met the six nurses stationed there. Inasmuch as I was to return to Juneau, I could visit several islands and village nurses later.

There were thirty-seven nurses, eighteen stationed at hospitals or school infirmaries. Twelve were village nurses who functioned either in clinic room or as visiting nurses in the village. Nine others were itinerant nurses who made two trips a year, one in winter by dog sled and one in summer by gas boat. Both Indians and Eskimos move around a good deal, following the game for pelts and the fish for food. There is not much employment except where there is a fish cannery.

The itinerary that we worked out was to proceed by commercial boat across the Gulf of Alaska to Seward, thence by rail to Mountain View, then by private bush plane at Anchorage for Dillingham, thence to Bethel on the Kuskakwim River, thence down to Hooper Bay, thence to Mountain Village, thence to Unalakleet, thence to Golovin and to Nome. At Nome I was to board the *North Star* and proceed to Kotzebue and on up to Point Barrow, then back to Nome. From Nome I was to fly to Fairbanks, by boat on the Yukon to Tanana and Nulato and back, thence by bush plane to Tetlin and back to Fairbanks, and back to Juneau by a big plane. I will fill in this outline. The boat up to Seward was very comfortable, but the Gulf of Alaska was anything but comfortable. We touched at Yakutat, but the nurse there, Miss Knickerbocker, was "outside" on vacation. It was customary for Alaska personnel to accrue their annual leave for three years so that they had enough time and money to get back "to the states" for three months. We touched at Cordova, where I saw Nurse Reese on dock for about half an hour. I was so pea green with the ocean's nasty motion that she gave me much more sympathy and understanding than I could convey to her, I am sure. The trip across the gulf was unusually bright and clear, and the snow-capped mountains were wonderfully impressive. I dragged myself out to see a glacier at Yakutat but retreated with all possible speed as soon as the boat got under way again.

On the same boat I met Mrs. Dunbar, the executive secretary of the Anti-Tuberculosis Association of Portland, Oregon. She had friends at Seward who took us in for the three days we were there waiting for the once-a-week train to Fairbanks. They were most kind about showing us the sights of Seward. The houses were not large, but they were snug. The gardens were very fine. Almost every house had a small greenhouse which gave them a head start with their gardens. The flowers were unusually large owing to the long days of sunshine. The train up to Mountain View was a narrow-gauge line and ran only during the day. It tied up for the night, and the passengers slept in a hotel. The journey was unusual because the train stopped to allow the passengers to pick flowers and crawled along in a very leisurely fashion.

The nurse at White Mountain served the boarding-school pupils and the nearby Indian settlements. Her activities were based on the instructions from a contract doctor from Anchorage. I thought she was doing a good job, considering how much she was alone on the job. It was primitive technique. I was there three days. I ordered a nursing bag for her.

At Anchorage I met the bush plane that was to carry me with stopovers up to Nome. It was on pontoons, and

I went down the rocky beach and, having no hip boots, was carried piggy-back out to the plane. I had to make a long leg up into the plane. There were six seats, and I sat next to the pilot. We roared off the water across Cook Inlet, through a narrow canyon in a drizzling rain. One could almost have touched the canyon walls. Finally we came to Iliama Lake and spent the night there. We stayed at the Road House which resembled a large Pullman car—berths on each side of the room behind calico curtains. One didn't care to use a flashlight to undress. There was a big pot-bellied stove down at one end, with kitchen and dining table beyond. The toilet facilities were outside, and then one was glad of a flashlight. Just thinking what it was like in the dead of winter gave one pause. The next morning we took off for Kanakanak, a small village near Dillingham. The hospital there served a scattered population of 1,500 to 1,800, largely Eskimos. There were two nurses. The doctor made field trips, and one nurse made field trips in winter, when more of the people stayed at home. They scattered far and wide in the fishing season. There were only twelve hospital beds, and the nurses lived on the top floor, taking turns on call at night.

From there we flew over to Bethel on the Kuskakwim River. The nurse, Mrs. Lula Heron, had been there for fifteen years. She was very interested in helping the tuberculosis children. There was no hospital there, but there should have been. Mrs. Heron had developed many outside contacts in the interest of her work. When I was there she was desperately afraid that her supply of cod-liver oil, coming from friends in Philadelphia, would miss the last boat in. The anxiety over supplies being delayed was omnipresent.

From Bethel we crossed over to Mountain Village on the lower Yukon. There was a good doctor, Dr. Corthell, who had a large area to cover. He was very anxious that I go down to Hooper Bay, where one of his visiting nurses was trying to handle a typhoid epidemic, so I went. What a spectacle it was. An Eskimo village of driftwood shacks. The poor nurse was trying to teach the Eskimos to care for the sick, control the spread of infection, disinfect the excreta, and get clean food for herself. I never saw more dogged, valiant service. I really longed to roll up my sleeves and help her. Back in Mountain Village I certainly gave her a warm word of approval. I think Dr. Corthell was pleased that he had showed me how difficult life could be for a nurse in Alaska. There were eighteen beds at Mountain Village. The wooden hospital was built on a glacier, and one end of it heaved and sank during the year sometimes as much as twenty-seven inches. The chimneys fell apart, and the wind blew through the building with more of a gale than a draft. It really was a wreck of a place.

Flying over Alaska was very interesting. We saw several bands of caribou. The terrain looked awfully soggy, and one could easily sense the impossibility of being found if a forced landing on some little lake had to be made. One felt much safer with pontoons than with wheels. The trees did not look inviting, and the muskeg (wet, boggy land) looked pretty soft. One did not wonder that the *esprit de corps* of the flyers brought about a high quality of search for lost planes. As we flew up the Yukon we saw little flocks of white tents on the riverbanks—clusters of natives fishing for winter food for themselves and their dogs. We could even see the racks where the fish were drying.

We stopped at Nulato to refuel, and I had a half day there with the nurse, Mrs. Brady. She had a few infectious diseases to deal with, but her main problems included accidents, respiratory infections, obstetrics, infant care, and environmental sanitation. There was a Catholic school there. Mrs. Brady wanted a pair of scales, and she needed equipment to take Wassermann tests, though there was said to be less syphilis than gonorrhea. Patients from the many little villages had to be flown to some hospital after the freezeup, if they would go. This responsibility was part of the nurse's work. In summer the patients could be taken by gas boat if there was time for a long trip. The net result was that only elective surgery, hernia, etc., was recommended. Emergency cases usually could not be arranged in time. Flying was expensive. All this entailed good judgment and intelligent persuasion on the part of the nurse. All these arrangements had to be cleared by radio with the hospital and the central office in Juneau.

One heard an endless amount of Japanese music interspersed with the most personal messages from faraway stations. The nurses had their own receiving and sending sets, which they took with them. I heard a message from a Mrs. Smith to her husband to find her diamond ring and send it by air to Juneau, along with her fur coat, in time for her departure by boat for the states. All of Alaska knew about it. I suppose that nothing wrought greater changes in Alaska than airplanes and the radio.

From Nulato we flew to Unalakleet, where the nurse, Miss Hayes, had a busy clinic. Unalakleet is an old settlement and a trading crossroads between Indians and Eskimos. It seemed almost citified by comparison with the usual small village. There were wide sidewalks, not many of which were those precarious duck boards two feet wide. Mrs. Brady made a few field trips—not long distances away. She knew her work well and got along better with the natives than with the few white people at the school.

From Unalakleet we flew across Norton Bay to Galovin and thence to Nome. As we were flying across Norton Bay, we saw a white whale swimming along deep in the water.

159

Of course, I felt very Moby Dickish and got the pilot to circle it several times. I even took movies of it.

At Nome there was a small mission hospital served by the contract doctor. There was also a dispensary where the natives could see the nurse. She could send them, if necessary, to see the doctor at his office between 1 and 3 P.M. He saw only patients who came with a note from the nurse. This practice saved him much time and useless listening to nonmedical problems. The second nurse made trips out to villages during such times as she expected to find the Eskimos at home. When I was in Nome, there were a lot of Eskimos from King Island camping on the beach, carving walrus ivory for the tourist trade. I bought a few delightful miniature animals. The King Islanders could make quite a little money this way and of course enjoyed the "city life" for the summer months. Their camps were canvas tents. An overturned skin boat protected most of their gear. The permeating smell of seal oil could not be escaped. They used it to make fried bread, to preserve food, and to grease their boots to make them waterproof.

The *North Star* was making ready to sail to Point Barrow, so there was considerable excitement among the Eskimos because we would go near enough to King Island to take them almost there. They would be met by skin boats from the Island and thus make it home before freezeup.

This section of the journey was complicated by danger from icebergs which might be driven toward shore, so a constant lookout was going on from the prow of the boat day and night. The captain and first officer were more apprehensive than they had been earlier. One could feel the tightening up all through the passage. The eighth of September was the deadline for arrival at Point Barrow, so we stopped very briefly on the way up. We stayed one-half day at Teller, and I had a walk on the beach and saw quite

160

a few sights, a string of ferocious dogs chained to a log cabin, racks of fish drying, an Eskimo mother making fried bread on a little campfire, and some delightful toddlers staggering around on the beach begging for chewing gum or candy. All chewing gum was common property among the Eskimos, so they picked up their immunity at an early age. If one believed in the hypothesis of immunity in connection with the germ theory, it alleviated some of the shock connected with one's observations. Kill or cure was an accepted law of nature. So we sailed on in sight of Russia's Big Diomede Island, around Cape Prince of Wales, across the Arctic Circle to Point Hope, thence up to Point Barrow without stopping at any way stations. We had to stand off about one mile from shore at Barrow and run toward the beach in the captain's launch, then transfer to a skin boat and land in about two feet of water. I was carried like a sack of meal by a sturdy little Eskimo and deposited on dry land.

The hospital at Point Barrow had been a Presbyterian mission venture and had just been transferred to the government. The doctor had left, and an epidemic of dipththeria was being managed by a good sort of native practical nurse. She devoted many hours of work, but naturally her judgment was limited. I talked with the head of the mission and with Mr. Brower, the trader of many years' standing. The Signal Corps officer and his family were going out with us to stateside so I got an earful of the seamy side. It took a day to unload the supplies. Everybody worked hard.

The school yard was full of roly-poly children who were excited at having a new audience. Their pleasure was infectious. There might be one more boat before winter shut them off, so the mission was hoping their supplies would get in too. Perhaps the Coast Guard cutter might

161

be in also. The Coast Guard cutter usually carried a Public Health Service doctor and an Indian Service nurse on their trips and always did quite a lot of medical work both among the natives and the white people stationed wherever it touched. Their help was much appreciated.

While at Point Barrow we went in a gas launch over to see the remains of the Wiley Post airplane accident. It had occurred just two weeks before I got there. The plane was standing on its nose in shallow water, a sad mark of tragedy. One realized anew the dangers of the North. And we were even more impressed with the caution and courage of Captain Whitlam, who made this Arctic trip every year in the *North Star*.

On the way back we stopped at Point Lay, where I had sent a nurse, Miss Tiber, the year before. She took me to visit several families in the village, where she had saved one case for me to see. A woman had broken a needle off in her finger, and it was infected. I was the supervisor on trial. Would I transgress the unwritten law of nursing and medical practice? I opened the finger without any novo-caine, and out popped the needle and quite a lot of bloody pus. I can't say that I enjoyed the procedure, but the patient enjoyed the almost immediate relief and agreed to keep on the hot, wet Epsom salts dressing. Of course, we couldn't stay to see the end results of my surgery. I was mean enough not to let Miss Tiber know that I had seen through her ruse. I pretended that it was just deference to a super-visor on her part. We let it go like that. I don't believe I would have tackled an appendix abscess!

Our next stop was at Point Hope. There was no nurse there. An Episcopal mission station was established, and the clergyman proudly showed us his coffin being used as a clothes closet until such time as its proper use should be necessary. He was also inordinately proud of his cemetery, which was surrounded by a fence made of whale jaw bones. The visit was slightly macabre but added to my knowledge of the effects of isolation.

At Kivalina we stopped to take on reindeer for freezing to be stored at Nome and later distributed to the natives living farther south. The round-up was ready for the men to begin their shooting. The Eskimos were there to dress and pack the carcasses on the *North Star*. The camp was for two days. The sailors all helped. The reindeer were slow and didn't even try to stampede when one fell. We had a wonderful stew of reindeer tongues for dinner, and the native helpers had liver stew. Of course, the purpose of the shoot was to weed out the herd, which had grown so big that there was not enough moss for them.

In the evening the crew of sailors and the Eskimos put on a dance in the community house, music by phonograph. There was one overheated spot near the stove. The Eskimos were persuaded to sing and dance for us. The women danced with their hands, while the men did the footwork, not too different from that of the North American Indians. The songs were long ballads about hunting adventures and about the women's and the children's waiting for the hunters' return.

The next stop was Kotzebue. The whole town was down on the beach to welcome us. The nurses were in uniform for my benefit, and the women citizens were in cotton dresses with fur jackets or parkas. The children raced back and forth, and one boy demonstrated his skill on a bicycle on the pebbles of the beach. The men were in work clothes with rubber hip boots, ready to help unload the skin boats. The supplies were loaded onto stout wooden sleds and dragged up to the village by the men.

Again the rope ladder overside and the leap into a skin boat at just the right moment. The audience on shore was delighted.

At Kotzebue there was a twenty-bed hospital under the supervision of Dr. Smith, a competent surgeon. There were two hospital nurses and two itinerant nurses. The traveling nurses came in for relief work in hospital during the summer. This hospital served a large territory, a population of about two thousand. It was the most active station I visited, with an X ray of sorts. Of course, there were lots of makeshifts, but the staff all pulled together. We had a light snowfall while I was there, and they dressed me up in a wonderfully smelly parka and loaded me properly on a dog sled, and we took off at a gallop with a native driver running alongside to keep the sled right side up and the dogs from fighting. That contributed to my experience and knowledge of what the traveling nurses had to do on their winter trips. The tides and currents were so swift at Kotzebue that the gas boats had to have good engines. A lame boat meant a dangerous trip. The Eskimo lacks the benefit of oaths, and when the engine coughs and dies he exclaims "Oh my!" They are delightful people, love to tease, and get a rise our of you if they can.

I find this memorandum of the traveling nurse's plan of work for one winter:

Leave Kotzebue in September by boat to Noatuk, 20 hours in a small native power boat. By dog team two days in Kivalina, return to Kotzebue by Christmas, 3 days by dog team. In January fly 1½ hours to Shungwak. In February 5 days by dog team to Selawik. March—1 day by dog team to Noorvik and return. April—by dog team—detour and return to Kotzebue

164

65 miles by dog team just before break-up. Fly to Sela-wik—45 minutes—after break-up. One trip up the river to fish camp in May.

The process of getting ready for a trip in winter, besides securing clothing, was to get the meals cooked and frozen and arranged in order in boxes so that they would fit right back in the fry pan. They took a primus (gasoline) stove because wood was hard to find. There were log shelters along the route, sometimes buried in snow. Axes, picks, and shovels were indispensable. Food for the dog teams had to be carried along too. It all sounded unbelievably rugged. The nurses usually stayed with the school teachers or traders or missionaries. They carried a few drugs but depended on the schools for most of their supplies. When they left, the teachers carried on. With a radio the teachers were able to get some medical advice from the nearest doctor.

The nurses tried to get to each school twice each year. Hours were spent getting ready to go—days spent going, and often days spent waiting for patients to turn up. The nurses tried to teach cleanliness to midwives, but it was uphill work all the way.

In Kotzebue I got much more insight into the problems and solutions as worked out than at any other unit, because I saw more nurses.

On the way back to Nome we did not stop at Shishmaref, but we heard a nice story about the new missionary. The Eskimos said they liked him because he taught them how to cheat the trader. This was because he taught them how to send their down feathers to Montgomery Ward, where they got more money than the traders would give them.

From Nome I flew to Fairbanks, going down the Yukon in a small commercial boat to see the Tanana Hospital. It was small, twelve beds, and more Indians were cared for than Eskimos—more tuberculosis and accidents than other conditions. As I recall it, they did very little surgery.

Then I flew to Tetlin to see one of the other nurses I had sent up from Arizona, Miss Sanstrom. I enjoyed my visit. I stayed there for an entire week because I couldn't get out. The ice started to form on the river, and I was really petrified for fear I wouldn't get out at all. When the airplane appeared overhead, I was much relieved. I had seen enough, and the snow was flying the day we left. We stopped one place to pick up some gold to carry into Fairbanks—two packages about the size of two pounds of sausage, but weighing six hundred pounds. The runway was short, and with the extra weight of the gold we just barely made it over the treetops.

Fairbanks was a livelier town than Nome. I would have enjoyed more time there, but I was anxious to get outside. The toil and moil, the courage and the stamina, of all those nurses was really overwhelming. The Indian Service in the states was a paradise by comparison.

I take from my notes of twenty-eight years ago a little of one nurse's experience on a field trip down in the lower Yukon territory.

Made 14 villages that trip. A native driver with dog team. January 12th, first village with 8 homes, 60 people. Three days there and then to a fish village. Visited every home. Many families away hunting for skins. Only two families there. Stayed a few hours then to Old Hamilton. 12 families. Stayed one week, making a side trip to Kotlek where there were 5 houses but only one family at home. Stayed a week at trader's. Quite a few white people, 30 natives—50 natives a mile and a half away, 70 to 80 natives an hour away.

One should allow more than a week. At Akulurak spent 2 nights and 1 day. Mission boarding school of 100 pupils. Went to 3 homes in a trapping camp. No lights in turf houses. Got to Pastolic in 5 hours. 30 people. Spent night at trader's Then to Black River, one village of 7 homes. No place to stay, so on to Scarruion Bay. From 7 A.M. to 4 P.M. to get there. 100 people. Stayed one week at school. Left at 7 A.M. for Hooper Bay over mountains, going into storm. Driver didn't know the way. No trail. Very thick. John finally found a house. No axe or shovel. Took an hour to get in. Snow drifted in and covered stove. Next day stormy so did not venture out. Third day cleared. Got out and made Hooper Bay at 5 P.M. Stayed a month—about 200 people there. Tried to get to Chevak which is flat and has no landmarks. After 3 days missed the village entirely. Started for home 70 miles away. Knew 2 landmarks, a little elevation, a large lake. Fog obscured everything. No trail. Dark came in and had to dig into snow with hatchet. The weather was mild. Slept in willows on river bank. About noon found a faint crooked hunter's trail. Finally turned back after 2 miles, found a tin can on stick with directions that could be followed. Glad to arrive back at Mountain Village the evening of second day.

Lots of work for very little real achievement for people needing help.

I flew from Fairbanks to Juneau. While at Juneau I visited the nurses stationed on the nearby islands, Hoonah, Sitka, and Angoon. These islanders maintained old habits, although many of the old ceremonial customs had disappeared. The Thlingit Indians and the Russian-Indian mixed bloods were prevalent. Many still lived in long houses. They worked at fishing and in canneries and were very competent with boats. At Sitka the remains of Russian occupation were the most noticeable, but at this time they were becoming mere vestiges of a former heyday. After three weeks I returned to Seattle by a commercial steamer, the S.S. *Alaska*.

I'd had all I could take in and more than I could digest. I felt more dirty than tired and was worn through at the elbows, ragged at the cuffs, and needed something—I didn't know what—more than a wash and a wave. Perhaps a new skin was the answer.

XXVIII

Good-by to Uncle Sam

IN 1937 MY SISTER WANTED ME TO QUIT WORK, and she offered to set up two annuities which would furnish an income on which I could live simply. I had lived simply before. I had seen older women who stayed in harness because of necessity, and I didn't look forward to eighteen more years of grinding out the time until I would be eligible for retirement, which was then at seventy-two years of age or thirty years of service. The red tape was becoming more burdensome. I had really achieved my objectives of finding nurses. The turnover was still considerable, but the net was good. I wanted a few years while I was still vigorous to pursue a private life, so I accepted my sister's offer and said that in a year's time I would be ready to leave. This was a big change. I looked forward to it.

Naturally I also looked back and realized the many factors that had gone into the success of my venture. I did not want to live in Washington, and I figured that I could sell my house there and find another place to live, preferably somewhere in the West.

This story of my recollections does not in any way begin to give credit to the many, many nurses I found to invest their energies in hard work. They felt the needs and put their shoulders to the wheel. They made the success. If the Congress had not changed its purpose by making funds available to implement medical service, we could not have moved forward. When I entered the service, there were only fifteen graduate nurses. When I left, there were six hundred and fifteen. I found them, and the Congress paid them, and they carried the load.

Also this doesn't begin to describe the help that I had from the supervisory nurses in the districts. Miss Sallie Jeffries, Miss Mabel Morgan, Miss Mary McKaye, and Miss Elizabeth Duggan were all wise and temperate women on whose judgments I could depend.

Another large factor in my securing nurses was the great depression, which made for a much more eager acceptance of employment than had been usual. A government job spelled some sort of security.

I could not have functioned without the guidance of the doctors, both those in the Indian Service and those loaned by the Public Health Service. It was a period of expansion. It came with a rush. Plenty of satisfaction, plenty of work, and plenty of fun.

I have never regretted the years spent in the Indian Service. The problems, the way of living, the travel, the almost kaleidoscopic changes in perspective, and the variety of people suited my temperament. I was happy and knew it.

The Western Frontier Library

of which *The Indians and the Nurse* is Number 28, was started in 1953 by the University of Oklahoma Press. It is designed to introduce today's readers to the exciting events of our frontier past and to some of the memorable writings about them. The following list is complete as of the date of publication of this volume:

1. Prof. Thomas J. Dimsdale. *The Vigilantes of Montana*. With an introduction by E. DeGolyer.
2. A. S. Mercer. *The Banditti of the Plains*. With a foreword by William H. Kittrell.
3. Pat F. Garrett. *The Authentic Life of Billy, the Kid*. With an introduction by Jeff C. Dykes.
4. Yellow Bird (John Rollin Ridge). *The Life and Adventures of Joaquín Murieta*. With an introduction by Joseph Henry Jackson.
5. Lewis H. Garrard. *Wah-to-yah and the Taos Trail*. With an introduction by A. B. Guthrie, Jr.
6. Charles L. Martin. *A Sketch of Sam Bass, the Bandit*. With an introduction by Ramon F. Adams.
7. Washington Irving. *A Tour on the Prairies*. With an introduction by John Francis McDermott.
8. *X. Beidler: Vigilante*. Edited by Helen Fitzgerald

Sanders in collaboration with William H. Bertsche, Jr. With a foreword by A. B. Guthrie, Jr.

9. Nelson Lee. *Three Years Among the Comanches*. With an introduction by Walter Prescott Webb.

10. *The Great Diamond Hoax and Other Stirring Incidents in the Life of Asbury Harpending*. With a foreword by Glen Dawson.

11. *Hands Up; or, Twenty Years of Detective Life in the Mountains and on the Plains:* Reminiscences by General D. J. Cook, Superintendent of the Rocky Mountain Detective Association. With an introduction by Everett L. DeGolyer, Jr.

12. Will Hale. *Twenty-Four Years a Cowboy and Ranchman in Southern Texas and Old Mexico*. With an introduction by A. M. Gibson.

13. Gen. James S. Brisbin, U.S.A. *The Beef Bonanza; or, How to Get Rich on the Plains*. With a foreword by Gilbert C. Fite.

14. Isabella L. Bird. *A Lady's Life in the Rocky Mountains*. With an introduction by Daniel J. Boorstin.

15. W. T. Hamilton. *My Sixty Years on the Plains*. With an introduction by Donald J. Berthrong.

16. *The Life of John Wesley Hardin, As Written by Himself*. With an introduction by Robert G. McCubbin.

17. Elizabeth Bacon Custer. *"Boots and Saddles"; or, Life in Dakota with General Custer*. With an introduction by Jane R. Stewart.

18. John F. Finerty. *War-Path and Bivouac; or, the Conquest of the Sioux*. With an introduction by Oliver Knight.

19. Frederic Remington. *Pony Tracks*. With an introduction by J. Frank Dobie.

20. Thomas Edgar Crawford. *The West of the Texas Kid*. Edited and with an introduction by Jeff C. Dykes.

172

21. Frank Collinson. *Life in the Saddle*. Edited and arranged by Mary Whatley Clarke. With drawings by Harold D. Bugbee.
22. *Fifty Years on the Trail: A True Story of Western Life*. The adventures of John Young Nelson as described to Harrington O'Reilly.
23. Edward Bonney. *The Banditti of the Prairies: A Tale of the Mississippi Valley*. With an introduction by Philip D. Jordan.
24. Walter Baron von Richthofen. *Cattle-raising on the Plains of North America*. With an introduction by Edward Everett Dale.
25. Captain Charles King, U.S.A. *Campaigning with Crook*. With an introduction by Don Russell.
26. *Life of Tom Horn, Government Scout and Interpreter, Written by Himself: A Vindication*. With an introduction by Dean Krakel.
27. Edward Everett Dale. *Cow Country*.
28. Elinor D. Gregg. *The Indians and the Nurse*.

The text for *The Indians and the Nurse* has been set on the Linotype in 10-point Times Roman, a highly legible type designed by Stanley Morison. The paper on which this volume is printed bears the University of Oklahoma Press watermark and has an effective life of at least three hundred years.